S0-CMW-189

This is an ancient symbol representing THE SIX DIRECTIONS OF SPACE.

SCIENCE for the NON-SCIENTIST

by

A. R. PATTON

Professor of Chemistry

Colorado State University

Fort Collins

BURGESS PUBLISHING COMPANY

426 South Sixth Street • Minneapolis 15, Minnesota

Library of Congress Catalog Card Number 62-19188

Third Printing 1963

Preface

This little textbook has been written for non-science majors who have had no previous courses in the sciences or in mathematics. It grew out of a conviction that conventional courses in beginning chemistry, physics, or physical science do not adequately meet the needs of certain students who will not become scientists, technologists, or engineers, but need to know something of what science is about in order to become intelligent citizens in an Age of Science. It is intended primarily for use in a course taught by the author at Colorado State University, which is entitled Natural Science. This is a one quarter five credit course, consisting of approximately fifty lecture and discussion periods.

The task of natural science is to describe the behavior of the physical world. Scientists describe the physical aspects of reality in terms of four concepts: space, time, matter, and energy. This book is organized around these four concepts. Although the subject matter area is physical science, the applications and examples wherever possible are drawn from biochemical sources, reflecting the author's many years of research and teaching in biochemistry, and his personal interest in chemistry and mankind. The book is not intended to compete with the many larger textbooks for traditional courses in physical science, usually one year courses.

Nowadays to be an educated person one must be literate in science. Every educated person needs to have at least an elementary understanding of the concerns of his compatriots in other areas of knowledge and culture. It is hoped that this book sheds light on the scientific world-view and the spirit of science in a way which will be accessible to the general reader without any scientific background.

A. R. Patton

Fort Collins, Colorado
June 1962

Contents

Chapter 1 The Image of Science

When a person has been taken somewhere while unconscious, perhaps to a hospital, upon regaining consciousness the first question he asks is, "Where am I?" Each person pictures himself with a certain location in space. This may extend a few feet, or thousands of miles, depending upon his experience and knowledge. The second question a person usually asks is, "What time is it?" He wants to know not only <u>where</u> he is, but <u>when</u> he is. In such a case, he may be satisfied to be told the date on the calendar and the time by the clock. Often, however, one's location in space and time is enriched by knowledge and experience of events which may have happened long ago and far away.

Each individual usually believes his world and himself to exist exactly as they appear to him, but that does not make it so. What has just been described is a personal image. Each of us has such an image of himself and the world around him. No two images are alike, since they are built from our experiences, and each of us has a different pattern of experience. Nevertheless, the nature of our image is very important, because it is a factor in determining our behavior. If our image is false, or incomplete, our behavior is likely to be defective. For example, one frequently reads of a shooting accident, in which was involved the false image of the gun in question: "I didn't know it was loaded."

We are living in an Age of Science. We are part of a scientific society. Science and technology have become a dominant force in our social order. Our destiny is irrevocably associated with understanding and use of scientific knowledge. For this reason a correct image of science--what science is, what it can and cannot do, how scientists think--has become of supreme importance. This need was thrust upon us suddenly by the breakthrough in release of nuclear energy. Many false images of science are in circulation. The gap between the scientists and the decision makers is widening. This must be viewed with alarm.

How is one to improve his image of science? The first problem is that science deals with what the average person believes to be the real world. So the problem becomes first of all one of understanding what is meant by reality. Like everybody else, the scientist must deal with the physical world entirely by means of his sense perceptions, the gateways to the mind. Chiefly, the sense perceptions consist of seeing, hearing, tasting, smelling, and touching. All that we know of the physical world comes to us through these senses. The peculiar thing is that the sense messages are all alike: they are merely tiny electric currents. It is the place in the brain to which they go that tells us whether they are seeing, hearing, tasting, smelling, or touching.

Plato described each self as imprisoned in the body like an oyster in its shell. Each scientist, too, is a prison in which a prisoner dwells, surrounded by the world around him. The way in which the scientist receives messages through his sense perceptions from the outside world can be likened to two prisoners in adjacent cells, who send messages to each other by tapping on the wall. The wall between them is what keeps them apart, and at the same time it is their means of communication. Although the average man views what he sees of the material world as being real, it should be noted that science makes no such assumption. Rather, science views the material world not so much as reality itself, as a barrier lying between man and reality, at the same time being man's only scientific means of communicating with reality.

To some it may come as a shock to learn that science does not deal principally with facts. Science deals with concepts. The glory of science is not its facts, but its concepts. In the sense that the word "explain" means, "tracing back to origin and cause," science does not explain, it only describes. It is oversimplification to say that science deals with cause and effect. Science relates one thing to another, one process to another process, one event to another. The judgment as to which is cause and which is effect lies outside the field of science, although it is not always outside the area of decision of the human being who calls himself a scientist. Science cannot answer "Why?", which is why it cannot answer the ultimate question, "Why am I?" This is one of the many limitations of science. It can never deal directly with values, nor can it ever reach ultimate ends. Science is always incomplete and tentative. When the word "why" appears in a science text, it is to be interpreted as meaning "how come?" rather then "what for?" In other words, science deals with mechanism, but not with purpose.

Science does not deal with the whole of life. There are many kinds of human experiences, and science can deal with only a portion of them. Specifically, the task of science is to describe the behavior of the material (or physical) world. The great problem here is a problem of communication. It is at this point that the breakdown often comes.

Both scientists and artists are creative, but they differ in their attempts to communicate. The artist hopes to express his idea in such a manner that each recipient will be stimulated to recreate it in his own way. He would not expect two persons to get exactly the same meaning from a symphony or a painting. The scientist, on the other hand, hopes to express his idea in such a way that it will mean exactly the same thing to all persons in all times and places. That is why he usually uses the precise language of mathematics.

The physical scientist differs from the historian and the biological scientist in respect to the one-time event. Physical science deals with "what happens," while history deals with "what has happened." In order to be accepted in physical science, an event must be experimentally repeatable and must happen the same way each time. Thus, it is scientific to say, "Ice floats on water," because any piece of ice floats on any body of water any time it is tried. If this had been observed only once, it could be a part of history but not a part of physical science. It is for this reason that physical science simply has nothing to say about a subject such as "The Virgin Birth."

The life-span of science has not been very long, and one might conceive of an event which repeats itself only every 10,000 years. It could have been observed by a scientist only once, if at all. Biological science is different from physical science, in that it deals entirely with one-time events. Each specimen of life is entirely unique. Thus biological science is closer to history and theology than to physical science. Sometimes the physical scientist insists that biological science is not a science at all, which would be true by this criterion. But it is not necessarily a sound criterion.

Like everybody else, the scientist must attempt to communicate by means of symbols. Most elegantly, these are mathematical symbols. Mathematics is the language of the scientist. But unfortunately, this is a foreign language to the average person, for whom the attempt at communication must be in words, and not too big words either. The science student or professional scientist might criticize this little book on the grounds that the author is a university professor, writing for university students, and accordingly he should abide by the rigorous standards of the world of science. If he had done so, this book would probably take 2000 pages, and nobody for whom it is intended would read beyond page five.

One of the first troubles we encounter is that so many of the words in use by scientists have a special meaning in science, quite different from their everyday meaning. Take the word "law," for example. In science, a law is merely a summary of experience, based upon careful observation of how nature behaves. It is nothing like the laws passed by a government, or any of the common meanings of the word. Here the mistake is on the part of the scientists, who perhaps should have chosen a less familiar word to mean "experience summary." Even the scientists themselves forget, and frequently speak of nature "obeying" certain "laws," as if nature were behaving in response to man-made commands.

The prestige of science has become so great that as soon as a new technical word is coined, the public takes it over and proceeds to use it in new, wrong ways, so that everyone is thoroughly confused as to what the word really means. Misuse of the words of science in this way is common in some areas of advertising. The average person is left in the helpless position of receiving a bombardment of scientific and pseudoscientific terms, without being capable of discriminating true from false. Aside from the frustration and deception which results, there is danger of mass acceptance of Science with a capital S, as a new religion which will bring about Utopia any day now, if only we act in faith like the south sea islanders who developed the new "religion" known as the "cargo cult" and put bamboo radio antennas on their shacks!

With continued familiarity, words lose their meanings and become merely stereotype symbols. A familiar brand of breakfast food is known as Quaker Oats. How unfamiliar it would seem to find packages on the food market shelves labelled "Methodist Oats," or "Presbyterian Oats!" A sign in a Woolworth store was observed to read, "Stainless Steel Silverware!" If one asks a group of children whether Mickey Mouse is a dog or a cat, there is usually someone who will say Mickey Mouse is a cat. These examples show how everyday words lose their meanings. The same thing happens to words of science.

The scientist communicates by means of symbols. Any perceivable object may be used as a symbol. Often a symbol is some kind of a mark on paper; this book is an attempt to communicate with words, which are one form of symbols. A symbol stands for a concept. A concept is a general notion about something. When a symbol is perceived by the senses, it triggers an association pattern in the mind of the recipient. When symbols begin to pile up, a group of scientists may get together and agree to use a new symbol to stand for a whole group of symbols. This new symbol is called a definition. This is one way to define definition. This practice is not something new with science; it is already old from use in theology and jurisprudence. This is why the layman often cannot understand theological or legal documents, even though many of the words may be familiar.

It is said that one can take a group of children out on a moonlight night, suddenly point and cry, "Look at the moon," and observe that many of the children will be looking at the pointing finger instead of the moon. A physician may write a prescription and hand it to a patient, saying, "Here, take this, I think it should help you." The patient leaves the office thoughtlessly chewing and swallowing the piece of paper on which the prescription was written! These are examples of confusing the word with the thing. In this book we are going to encounter trouble of this kind. We are going to deal with four main concepts of science. The symbols which stand for these four concepts are the words: space, time, matter, and energy. It is going to be necessary to keep in mind at all times that whenever these words are used they stand for the concepts.

We are living in a society in which the relation of the symbol to the concept is being destroyed, often with malicious intent. In the wake of the depth psychologists, a game is being played with symbols, for their own sake and for the sake of ideologies. Symbols for symbols for symbols are appearing, often with no real concept behind them. It thus becomes impossible to think in concrete terms any more. This purposeful distortion, by forces outside of science, is of concern to us at the moment only because it makes the problem of teaching about science all the more difficult. It is not easy to pin down concepts when the notion is abroad that one is free to behave like Humpty Dumpty in *Through The Looking-Glass*:

"When *I* use a word," Humpty Dumpty said, in rather a scornful tone, "it means just what I choose it to mean--neither more nor less."

"The question is," said Alice, "whether you *can* make words mean so many different things."

"The question is," said Humpty Dumpty, "which is to be master--that's all."

More often than not, the words used in science are actually metaphors. A metaphor is the most compact means of comparison: it is calling one thing another. More than we like to admit, we think in metaphors. For things of which we have no direct experience, such as the structure of an atom, we must speak in metaphors because we must reason by analogy. We think anthropomorphically in spite of ourselves, because we are human beings and that is the way our minds are made. We do thus because it is the best we can do. We all use metaphors in our everyday language. "The Lord is my shepherd" is an example of a metaphor. It is often overlooked that when a scientist calls something by a name, such as for instance "a sodium atom," this is a metaphor. Applying this label does not mean that he really knows what it is, in a deeper sense. In science, each generation learns a new set of metaphors.

Scientists assume certain things to be true without proof. These are the presuppositions of science. Even though the individual scientist may not be aware of these presuppositions, he is making use of them just the same. They are built into the framework of science laid down for him by his scientific forefathers, who did know these presuppositions. Briefly stated, the first three presuppositions of science are: (1) The behavior of the universe is orderly; (2) There is a cause for this orderly behavior; and (3) It is possible for the mind of man to know about this cause and behavior.

The presuppositions of science go back to the spiritual and social foundations of man. Modern science began in the seventeenth century. It grew out of beliefs held at that time. Of all things, there are some which can be perceived by the senses, or by scientific instruments such as the Geiger-Mueller counter which are really just extensions of the senses. Such things are known as matter, and they make up what we call the material world or the physical world. It is the belief of the great majority of mankind that there is a spiritual world behind this world of matter, even though it cannot be perceived by the senses. Belief in a spiritual world is the result of human experiences which lie outside the realm of science. Science does not deal with the whole of human experience.

This is not the place to go into the various "isms" of man, but it might be proper to mention three which are directly concerned with modern science. One group of persons denies the existence of the spiritual world. This is known as Materialism. Misunderstanding of the significance of science and technology has tended to lead mankind into Materialism. The opposite view, which denies the reality of the material world, is called Idealism. Plato was an

Idealist. Learned men of the Far East, in bygone centuries, achieved great experiential knowledge of the spiritual world, but held an attitude of indifference toward the material world which prevented them from developing leadership in physical sciences.

Neither complete Materialism nor complete Idealism could have been expected to lead to the new science which blossomed in seventeenth-century Europe and England. A third world-view was necessary, or rather a combination of these two views. In order to create a science which went beyond the materialistic pragmatism of the crafts, it was necessary to believe in the reality of the spiritual world which would lead to the basic presuppositions listed above. And in order to proceed with the task of comprehending the order and regularity of the physical world, it was also necessary to believe in the reality of matter and the importance of understanding its properties and behavior.

Nowadays when many seem to hold the view that a scientist who dares to use the word God is out of bounds, it may seem surprising to learn that the presuppositions which led to the new science, beginning in the seventeenth century and continuing to this day, were rooted in a firm belief in one God. In fact, there is ample historic documentation for the statement that modern science was an outgrowth of the Christianity of the time; although we shall not attempt to present such a case here. Although it is now possible to point out that the phenomena of the physical world might conceivably have grown out of Atheism, an examination of the lives and beliefs of the great founders of scientific thought will show that such an idea simply did not occur to them.

The belief in an orderly universe thus happened to follow from Monotheism, regardless of whether this was a prerequisite. At least, in the earlier times when people believed in many gods, who could change the laws of the world according to mere whim, studying science would not have been worth the trouble, and science as we know it could not have begun. Imagining what might have been the situation if this were true, Drummond wrote as follows in his Natural Law in the Spiritual World (1883):

"The sun might rise or it might not; or it might appear at any hour, or the moon might come up instead. When children were born they might have one head or a dozen heads, and those heads might not be on their shoulders--there might be no shoulders--but arranged about the limbs. If one jumped up in the air it was impossible to predict whether he would ever come down again. That he came down yesterday was no guarantee that he would do it next time. For every day antecedent and consequent varied, and gravitation and everything else changed from hour to hour. Today a child's body might be so light that it was impossible for it to descend from its chair to the floor; but tomorrow, in attempting the experiment again, the impetus might drive it through a three story house and dash it to pieces somewhere near the center of the earth."

The word science has many meanings. Originally, science meant knowledge of any kind. It referred to any organized body of knowledge. Thus we can have the science of ethics, the science of theology, or even the science of boxing. Historically, however, the particular branch of knowledge relating to the physical world and its phenomena, known as natural science or the science of nature, expanded so greatly that for most persons natural science became synonymous with science. For a person who was learned in natural science, a clergyman coined the new name, "scientist." Natural science is nowadays sometimes confused with "nature study," but it really means physics, chemistry, and the like.

To the average man, however, science means technology. Our confusion of science with technology reflects our emphasis on gadgetry and "know-how." It is often pointed out that most of the Nobel Prizes in science for new ideas go to foreign-born scientists, whereas most of those awarded to American-trained scientists have been for applied science or gadgets. In the early days at Cape Canaveral, the engineers publicly protested that every time a rocket or satellite launching succeeded, the press hailed it as a triumph of science, whereas every time it failed, the same press attributed this to engineering failure.

Thus the outcome of success in technology and engineering has been great prestige for science. As might be expected, "everybody wants to get into the act." New sciences are created almost daily, some of them genuine and some of them phony. In the universities, applied science flourishes while other areas languish. The education of science students, once cultural and scholarly, has become more and more vocational training for industry. It is becoming more difficult to tell a science graduate from an engineer. Cultural disciplines worthy of respect and support in their own right feel constrained to hide behind a façade of words pilfered from science. It is easier to get money, and recognition, for anything done in the name of science. Meanwhile the public has little appreciation for true science, and even less understanding of what it really is.

Probably some of our confusion of science with technology came about because somebody several decades ago decided that the way to teach science to school children was by the example of its end products. Thus for example, the Model T Ford automobile was held up as a product of science. Supposedly this would arouse the students to curiosity about metallurgy, thermodynamics, the calculus, chemistry, etc. It now seems clear that this was a mistake. Like the children looking at the finger instead of the moon, these children were led only to the faulty conclusion that one of the greatest American scientists was a man named Henry Ford! Edison who was not a scientist, is even to this day frequently hailed as a great American scientist. Meanwhile Willard Gibbs remains almost unknown. Although Willard Gibbs died in 1903, it was not until 1957 that his bust was finally placed in the American Hall of Fame. At the dedication ceremony, he was named as the greatest creative genius America has ever produced.

Questions

1. What is meant by the image of science?
2. Why is a correct image of science important to the non-scientist?

3. What does science have to say regarding the reality of the physical world?
4. Discuss some areas of human experience not covered by science.
5. What is meant by the word "why" as it is used in science?
6. What is meant by the word "law" in science?
7. Give examples of some metaphors used in science.
8. What are the presuppositions of science?
9. What is the difference between experimental and experiential?
10. What is the definition of "natural science?"

Chapter 2 The Image of the Scientist

We shall not be able to arrive at any clear-cut definition of a scientist. There is no accepted standard by which to judge whether a person is a scientist or not. One reason for this is the fact that unlike physicians, lawyers, veterinarians, chiropractors, engineers, and many others, the scientist does not need a license to practice. It is not suggested that licensing would clarify the situation, but unfortunately so far as the general public is concerned a scientist is anyone who can call himself a scientist and get away with it.

Surveys have revealed that the public has an image of the kind of lives scientists lead which is rather far from the truth. From the mass entertainment media, and from other sources, the scientist has received an unflattering a stereotype. Many believe that scientists are evil, that they do not have a normal home life, that they want to torture living things. Often the picture is of a "mad scientist." High school students came up with the alarming disclosure that a scientist does not have a pretty wife! He is a grind, a brain, an egghead; he thinks only of new more deadly means of destruction, and he is willing to betray his country to the enemy! People have seen too many movies of the Frankenstein type, and too many television commercials like the one of two cartoon characters, with a sign on their home which reads "Mr. and Mrs. Evil Scientist."

It may be a disappointment to learn that the typical working scientist today is young, has a wife (sometimes pretty!), a home and children, a car which he washes on Saturday and a lawn which he mows himself. He may go skiing, play golf, attend church, go to PTA meetings, play bridge, take part in civic affairs, watch movies, listen to concerts, watch television, read the Sunday comics, and enjoy friends and neighbors. In fact, to the casual observer he is usually not distinguishable from the average business or professional man or woman.

It need hardly be pointed out that a woman can be a scientist as well as a man. The scientist need not wear a white coat, have a long white beard, or speak with a foreign accent, although of course he can have all of these and still be a scientist. It is said that a scientist reaches the peak of his creative power somewhere soon after the age of twenty-seven. Physical scientists are now winning Nobel Prizes while younger than thirty. Our world is being recreated by scientists whose extreme youth is perhaps their most salient feature.

It is difficult for the public to understand what a pure scientist is--what makes him "tick." Frequently a scientist is asked "What are you trying to prove?" Or he may be asked, "What is it good for?" Such questions show complete lack of understanding of the basic purpose of science. A true scientist never tries to "prove" anything. He is only interested in learning the truth. A scientist does the work he does, because he is interested in doing it. That is what the ablest scientists really want to do if given the chance. Unfortunately, a lack of wisdom in policy and program can only too easily corrupt science's aims and hamper the able scientist in ways which are detrimental to everyone.

Whenever a person, with whatever scientific degrees, training, or experience, steps out of this role and accepts pay to gather evidence in support of an employer's preconceived position, without regard for truth, he is no longer functioning as a scientist. Since scientists are first of all human beings, it is to be expected that some persons with science degrees will be dishonest and willing to dupe the public for private gain. One should learn not to expect every statement uttered in the name of science to be the truth. Much of the deception now practiced would not be possible if the public were better informed about the fundamental principles of science.

The uninformed person may become confused by a legal decision directly involving some area of science or technology.

For purposes of law, it is necessary to set up legal standards which are officially correct, but at the same time may be scientifically inaccurate. The author was once asked to analyze a sample of disinfectant bearing a label stating that it contained fifty percent cresylic acid. A sample had been taken to the laboratory of an analytical chemist, who found by an accurate method that it contained only forty-seven percent. The purchaser felt he had just cause to sue. The trouble was that the analyst had not used the official method. This was the only method of analysis acceptable for legal use. By this method, the sample was found to contain fifty-one percent cresylic acid, more than the specifications required. Legal acceptance of a statement which appears to be in the realm of science is a technicality which does not in any way constitute proof that the statement is scientifically sound. In general, when conflict occurs between legal judgment and scientific theory, for practical purposes the legal judgment holds sway.

There is an old saying that people make two kinds of mistakes: Some people believe a thing is no good because it is new, and others believe a thing is no good because it is old. One should realize that just because something has recently been patented, this does not necessarily mean that it is an improvement over other products on the market. It may be just the opposite. The public generally does not understand about patents. The purpose of granting a patent is to induce the inventor to reveal secrets, by promising temporary protection. A patent is often defined as "a license to sue." That is, if one has a patent, this entitles him to sue someone who infringes on his patent. Most patents are never "reduced to practice." Just because an inventor, often a scientist, obtains a patent, this does not mean that it will make him wealthy. The whole field of patent law and theory is "tricky." Even though many processes and products resulting from research eventually receive patent protection, the important point to remember is that the mere granting of a patent should in no way be construed to imply either scientific merit or practical significance.

Since the average person suffers from the delusion that science deals only with "facts," he is seized with dismay when scientists disagree. He is inclined to feel that one scientist must be right, and the other one must be wrong. Actually, it is quite possible for two men of science to hold opposite views on an issue without one necessarily being right and the other wrong.

Glenn Seaborg, Chairman of the Atomic Energy Commission, illustrated this point with an example on a television interview with high school students. It concerned the danger of radioactive fallout from atmospheric testing of nuclear devices. This was not an actual case, but only an illustration. For the sake of argument, let us suppose that a given radioactive fallout had been estimated to cause one defect in one million births.

Two men of science try to evaluate the situation. One of them says, when compared with other omnipresent dangers, such as getting hit by a car when crossing the street, one chance in a million is so small as to be negligible. It is really quite insignificant, and one need not worry about it. After all, radioactive fallout in the form of cosmic rays from outer space and from natural radioactivity in the rocks has always been with us, and a person who moves from sea level to a high altitude city such as Denver, Colorado would probably get much more radiation from this move than he would ever get from nuclear tests.

The other scientist takes a different viewpoint. With equal justification from his viewpoint, he calculates that during the entire period that this fallout will be circling the Earth, it may be that 100,000 million babies will be born. Therefore 100,000 infants could be expected to be defective according to his reasoning, and now the number seems large and no longer negligible. Furthermore, he may say (stepping out of his role as a scientist now and speaking as a human being), the question is not whether the fallout from nuclear testing would be no more harmful than moving from San Francisco to Denver. The moral issue is whether one should be subjected to more radiation than he now gets where he now lives.

Hence scientists can honestly disagree. So long as they stick to areas of science, the cause of their disagreement is usually lack of sufficient experimental data. When sufficient data are available, it should be emphasized, scientists usually come to quick agreement all over the world. Thus Russian scientists and American scientists may disagree about systems of government, but they quickly reach full agreement about the interpretation of scientific data. There is no nationalism in science.

There is a tendency to assume that any scientist is competent in all fields of science. This is not so. Science is so vast and specialized that no scientist can cover more than a small area with any depth. But some scientists, when given the opportunity, freely express opinions concerning affairs about which they know little or nothing. It often happens that a scientist finds himself in the limelight because of some scientific discovery, and is then interviewed by the press and led into ill-advised comments in areas in which he is not well informed. This may be especially true when he speaks of social, military, or political policies, although of course there are scientists who keep informed in these fields and more are needed. But one must not believe that the scientist is competent to speak with authority about any subject merely because he is a scientist, even perhaps a Nobel Prize winning scientist. Granting that we are living in an Age of Science, nevertheless science and technology are at present receiving attention in the news out of proportion to their relative significance in the affairs of mankind.

Coupled with a belief in the omniscience of scientists is a belief that if given enough money science can do anything. Anybody who thinks that science can do anything, or carry out any order on command, simply doesn't understand science. This is like the old saying that if one ship can cross the Atlantic in five days, then five ships could cross the Atlantic in one day. This is one of the most dangerous and wasteful of fallacies about science. In order to achieve a scientific "breakthrough" in some area, it is thought that is needed, not merely money. Because of vagueness and ignorance about science, many problems are being attacked by spending money instead of thought. No amount of money will solve a problem if the scientific brainpower is missing.

There is a common opinion that science deals with certainties. Nothing could be further from the truth. Science does not deal with certainties; it only deals with probabilities. In science, judgment is eternally suspended, there is never a final word, and knowledge has an open end. Although the scientist tries to learn the truth, he never achieves this goal, but only pursues it. The best the scientist can do is to say that some described behavior is "extremely probable."

Science has a meaning for the word probability which differs from its everyday meaning. It is a mathematical concept. It is expressed numerically, as for example the ratio of the number of times one could expect a tossed coin to land "heads" to the number of times the coin is tossed. In the fallout example mentioned in a previous paragraph, the figure of one in a million was a probability, in the same sense as winning a lottery in which one million tickets had been sold.

If a scientist says something is "extremely improbable," he is not denying that it exists or that it can happen. He really means that it could hardly have happened due to chance. Chance produces disorganization. An organization can be defined as anything which is improbable. The most improbable creation known is man. If a deck of 52 playing cards is arranged in a certain sequence, and shuffling then begins, how many times would one have to shuffle before he could expect the cards to fall in the same sequence again due to chance? The answer is factorial 52, which means 1 X 2 X 3 etc. up to 52, a total of 8 followed by 67 zeros. This number is so fantastically large that to expect the event to happen at all is absurd. How much more absurd, from the standpoint of mathematical probability, would it be to expect an organization so wonderfully complex as a human being to occur by chance!

We have said that science deals with only a portion of human experience; experimental science (such as physics and chemistry) obtains this experience by means of what is known as an experiment. When a scientist does an experiment, he receives sense perceptions, often with the help of instruments. The data of an experiment are sense data.

But he does not count all the messages he receives as being a part of the experiment he is performing; he chooses which sense data to count and which sense data to ignore. He is often unaware that he is doing this, and he may say that what he has done is "designing the experiment with the objective in mind." But it is important to realize that all the time he is exerting his power of arbitrary choice.

To begin with a simple example, the scientist may have a headache on the day he performs the experiment, and he receives sense messages to this effect, but he chooses to ignore the headache as a part of the experience he will record. Of course the significance lies in his capacity to ignore far more subtle sense data than a headache. What he ignores can completely blind him to the truth, and often does. This is a chink in the armor of the scientist. He often does not realize himself how subjective he is in his choice of impressions. Some scientists are angered by the mere suggestion that their work might not be entirely objective at all times.

Nevertheless, the scientist is always subjective, even when he thinks he is being objective. From a philosophic viewpoint, the scientist is able to prove only that which he has presupposed. It is quite common for scientists to use statements in their research articles, books, or whatever they write or say, which seem quite unbecoming to the popular notion of science. They very commonly use expressions such as "I feel that," "I believe beyond the shadow of a doubt," "In my opinion," etc.

Sometimes we find a scientist ignoring something because he is not able to devise means of proving it by scientific methods. As a result, he may even come to deny that it exists. This is how some scientists arrive at a denial of the existence of God, love, a soul, etc. This has led to Scientism, which might be roughly described as a practice of classifying all information into two classes: (a) Science. (b) Nonsense. One must hasten to add that there is probably more Scientism outside the ranks of scientists than within.

This exercising of the power of choice helps explain how scientists have been so successful in accomplishing what they set out to do. They have been successful because first of all they have been very clever in choosing questions to answer which can be answered by the methods of science, and not choosing questions which science cannot answer, even though these may be the more important questions.

One might suppose that scientists are coldy factual and would not be caught dead using their imaginations, but on the contrary creative scientists use their imaginations as much as possible. They follow hunches, seek sudden flashes of insight, have dreams about their work, and arrive at notions by whatever means. Kekule is well-known as a chemist because he discovered the formula for benzene in a dream.

The story is told of a village in India from which an elephant had disappeared into the jungle. The villagers spent an entire day searching for the missing elephant, all except one fellow who was not considered to be very bright. He just sat. The next day, after all the others had abandoned the search, he went out and brought the elephant back. The other villagers crowded around with questions: "How did you know where to find the elephant?" "It was easy. All I did was to think, if I were an elephant, where would I have gone? Then I went there to look, and that is how I found the elephant." Scientists do like that. A chemist may think to himself, if I were such and such a molecule under such a situation, what would I do? Then he goes into the laboratory and makes tests to see if his idea was right. That is the way many discoveries are made. It must be pointed out that the scientist, through long and arduous training, has prepared himself by becoming as familiar as possible with the nature and habits of molecules in general, just as the villager who found the elephant was actually well acquainted with the habits of elephants.

Too much emphasis has been placed on the supposed importance of something called "the" scientific method. Elaborate rules are given, especially in books which most scientists never read, giving the steps to take in following the scientific method. Observation, generalization, deduction, examination, induction, hypothesis, theory, law, etc. are elaborated upon, in order that one may then define science in terms of "the scientific method." Unfortunately for those who depend upon use of "the scientific method" to prove that what they do is "science," there is not really any scientific method. Not in physical science, at least.

What there is, is more an attitude than a method. And it is an attitude which is commonly displayed with greater force and precision by nonscientists than by scientists, so it can hardly be called an attribute of science at all. The important point is that the scientist does not try to settle a problem by violence, by philosophizing, by oratory, by authority, or by taking a vote. The scientist's attitude is merely, "let's try it and see."

Here is a problem to illustrate this point. Suppose we have an encyclopedia of ten volumes, each volume exactly one inch thick, without covers or unnumbered pages. The pages are numbered in order, beginning with page one in volume one and going on through each volume to the last numbered page, which is at the end of volume ten. The ten volumes are lined up on a book shelf in the usual manner, the numbers on the backs reading from one to ten from left to right. Now suppose that an imaginary bookworm eats through the books in the shortest distance from page one to the last page. How many inches of books does the bookworm eat through?

The first obvious answer, when one merely thinks about it, like Aristotle would have done, is that the bookworm would eat through all the ten one-inch books, a total of ten inches. However, by lining up some actual books on a shelf (try it and see), we find that the correct answer is eight inches. Page one volume one is on the right-hand side, and the last page in volume ten is on the left-hand side, so the worm does not eat through either volume one or volume ten. In the author's experience, both beginning students and professional scientists tend to trip up on this one, when they answer without actually trying it with some real books.

In doing experiments, the scientist moves matter through space. In a literal sense all a man is capable of consciously doing is moving matter through space. Even if one sits quietly occupied with thought, he is consciously rearranging electrons from one location to another in his brain, and electrons are a form of matter as we shall see later. Of course it is not necessary that he be aware that he is transferring electrons; that is what he is doing nevertheless. This is not to say that all motion of matter through space is doing in the sense used here. Nor is all motion a result of conscious effort. As an outcome of this consideration, one could define science as the study of methods of controlled moving of matter through space, and how to apply mathematical probability to the consequences.

After a scientist has completed his experimental work, his work is still not complete. He must communicate his results to others. He must describe what he has observed. A scientist (a) chooses, (b) imagines, (c) does, and (d) describes. His communication is usually with other scientists in his own narrow field, by means of "papers" (lectures) presented at scientific meetings, or the publication of "articles" in technical journals. With the information explosion of science in recent years, so many scientists are publishing so much so madly that nobody can keep up with it. Part of this proliferation of words is caused by the practice of employers of scientists, who tend to judge their worth by the number of lines they publish per year. The entire world is being drenched with scientific (more or less) reports. They keep coming like the sticks carrying water in "The Sorcerer's Apprentice. Big Science thrives on publicity, and as a result the line between science and journalism has become blurred. As a consequence, if one wants to obtain a certain piece of scientific information, it is often easier to do the research over again than it is to try to find out if it has already been done and where it is published.

One final subject needs to be mentioned. This is the commonly-expressed idea that application of the scientific method to all problems of the world would bring about Utopia and that scientific progress will necessarily lead to happiness for all. Some of the greatest scientists of our time have pointed out flaws in this line of thinking. The fruits of science are a mixed blessing. For example, penicillin and the other antibiotics, the so-called "wonder drugs," have saved many lives. But in some countries, the lives of infants are being saved with the only result that they live long enough to die later of starvation. This is an unresolved problem, one of many in which science has created moral problems.

When the Wright brothers invented the airplane, they were opening a veritable Pandora's Box. If two wrongs don't make a right, in this case two Wrights "made a wrong." Now because of the jet plane, everybody in the world is breathing down everybody else's neck. If a passenger from Hong Kong develops small pox, passengers must be vaccinated all around the globe. The virus one picks up tomorrow may have come from Tokyo day before yesterday. The plane has scattered families all over the world, for both business and military reasons. Nowadays one does not need time to travel, only money. The consequence is an enormous increase in loneliness. A widow's son in the Navy is stationed in Guam for years. His mother must spend her savings to visit him for a few short weeks, a terrible sacrifice, followed by farewells which are heart-breaking.

Perhaps the whole situation was summarized by a recent cartoon showing two young ladies in a sports car, receiving a traffic citation from a policeman. One of the young ladies is saying to the other: "The radar showed we were going ninety miles an hour. I told you science doesn't lead to happiness."

Questions

1. Name a kind of scientist whom you would not want to be.
2. Give an example of a scientist acting in a dishonest manner.
3. What causes scientists to disagree?
4. Do you think scientists are spending money instead of thought?
5. Explain the statement that an organization is improbable.
6. What is the chink in the armor of a scientist?

7. How does a scientist try to settle a problem?
8. What is a person capable of consciously doing?
9. Name the four "features" of a scientist's experimentation.
10. Do you have a different image of science and scientists after reading these first two chapters?

Chapter 3 The Concept of Space

We are now living in The Space Age. It began abruptly on 4 October 1957, when the Russian unmanned artificial satellite Sputnik was launched into orbit around the Earth. The United States put a satellite into orbit on 31 January 1958. On 12 April 1961 the Russian airman, Yuri Gagarin, became the first human being to orbit the Earth. On 20 February 1962, John H. Glenn, Jr. circled the globe three times in the American space vehicle Friendship 7. Upon landing safely in the Atlantic ocean, he remarked, "It has been a long day, and I might add, a very interesting one." Later President John F. Kennedy said, "Space is an ocean upon which we must sail." Glenn's flight was repeated by Malcolm S. Carpenter on 24 May, 1962.

The effect of increased speed is to make the world seem smaller. In 1620 A.D., the Mayflower required 63 days to cross the Atlantic. Now jet planes do it in three hours. Commercial jet planes cruise just under the speed of sound, Mach 1, which is 760 miles an hour under standard conditions at sea level. To pass Mach 1 would not be economically feasible at present, because of the increased cost of the power required. Otherwise it could easily be done. The B-58 can go 1500 miles, the X-15 over 4000 miles per hour, and the Friendship 7 sped through space at more than 17,500 miles an hour. The Wright brothers flew about 25 miles an hour!

Noise is an unpleasant byproduct of fast air speed. Probably nothing in nature makes as loud a noise as aircraft. Planes convert about one percent of their engine power into sound. Fast planes pile heaped-up sound waves ahead of them, which send shock waves Earthward like giant claps of thunder. These explosions are called sonic booms. They frighten people and animals, and break windows.

In reference to The Space Age, the word <u>space</u> has a special meaning, as in space scientist, space suit, space vehicle, space flight, space station, space medicine, space psychology. This meaning of the word <u>space</u> is so new that it appears for the first time in the <u>Addenda</u> to Webster's New International Dictionary, Second Edition, 1960, along with other new words such as contrail, jato, radar, and snafu.

Long ago Aristotle taught that the earth was the center of the universe. Ptolemy built his teaching into an earth-centered scheme which held sway for 1500 years, with the support of the church. Galileo was convicted of heresy for daring to say that the Ptolemaic scheme was incorrect. We may laugh at those who believed that the earth was at the center and everything else revolved around it, but in a way we are demonstrating the same sort of man-centered tendency again in our special meaning for space. We are dividing the whole universe into two parts: (1) The earth and its atmosphere. (2) The remainder of the universe, which is now called space, or sometimes "outer" space.

It is difficult to focus on the scientific meaning of the word space because it is used metaphorically in everyday language. This has nothing to do with the concept of space. Instead it reveals something about human nature and the nature of human language.

We speak of <u>high</u> school, <u>higher</u> learning, <u>high</u> minded citizens, <u>low</u> quality merchandise, <u>low</u> moral standards, <u>high</u> accident rate, <u>high</u> fidelity sound, <u>narrow</u> minded persons, <u>shallow</u> personalities, <u>deep</u> thoughts, and "feelin' mighty <u>low</u>." Heaven is <u>above</u> and hell is <u>below</u>. The keys to the right on the piano play <u>high</u> notes (tones) and those to the left play <u>low</u> notes. The loudness of sound from a radio or television set is called <u>volume</u>, as if sound came by the gallon. These are examples of space metaphors.

Scientists are no better in this respect. They speak of high and low pressure, volume, temperature, humidity, reaction rate, polymers, energy, etc. Chemists speak of a reaction going forward or backward, as if it were an automobile. They speak of reaction "velocity," which implies that a chemical reaction has motion and direction in space, since velocity is what the mathematicians call a vector quantity. Chemists also ignore space in much of their theory, by assuming that the molecules of an ideal gas do not occupy space, or occupy so little space as to be negligible, which amounts to the same thing insofar as mathematical calculations are concerned.

Let us forget about space flight and space metaphors for the moment. Let us imagine an early man, sitting in the entrance to a cave, a very long time ago. Opposite the man, on the wall of the cave, is a spider. In the dim light the man sees the spider. Suddenly something happens in the man's brain, and he perceives the spider in a new relationship. He perceives the spider as a thing apart from himself. At that moment, he has invented what we mean by the concept of space.

We acknowledge that there may be some physical aspect of reality which is "real" space, but if so we do not know its true nature. All our ideas about space, such as distance and dimensions, hinge upon our own psychological abstraction, our mental construct, our concept which we refer to as "space."

Much of what goes by the name "space" involves primarily a feeling of distance. Ability to perceive objects apart leads to putting distance between them, and then inventing units to measure the distance. We have everyday units such as inches and miles, and jet hours. In December 1961, the American Association for the Advancement of Science met in Denver, Colo. Its official publication stated that Denver is located two jet hours from the west coast and four jet hours from the east coast. Perhaps the biggest and the smallest units are ones used by scientists: the light year and the Angström (rhymes with song-strum). A light year is the distance light travels in one year. Light travels 186,000 miles per second in a vacuum. This is equivalent to 6,000,000 million miles per year! The light year is the most common unit of distance used in astronomy. The optical telescope on Mount Palomar in California can observe light from galaxies or star clusters as far away as two billion light years. There are radio telescopes which can receive radio waves from eight or more billion light years away. Notice that the light year is a unit of distance and not a unit of time; one should not say light years ago.

A galaxy is a complex system of many stars. The galaxy in which we live is called the Milky Way. It is shaped like a hamburger bun 10, 000 light years thick and 100, 000 light years in diameter. It contains most of the stars we are able to see at night. But there is one of these stars which we can never see at night; we call this star the Sun. It is about 93 million miles away. Orbiting the Sun at 66,600 miles per hour is our own personal space vehicle, the planet Earth. In a true sense of the word we are all space travelers. The Milky Way is also spinning around. We are in orbit around the center of the Milky Way at the fantastic speed of 600, 000 miles an hour.

We feel intuitively that we know the nature of space. We feel that space is what lies all around us, above and below, to the right and the left, fore and aft. We learn in school that this space of common sense is called Euclidean space. We learn to plot it in three dimensions on x, y and z axes called Cartesian coordinates in solid geometry, straight lines extending to infinity and each at right angles to the other two. We use this kind of space when we build our houses, or buy cubic feet of natural gas to heat them, or gallons of gasoline and quarts of milk.

Unfortunately, our intuition does not tell us the truth about the nature of space. The old-fashioned, convenient kind of space we all live with and feel comfortable in turns out to be too good to be true. Einstein first suggested that light from stars would be deflected toward the Sun as the starlight passed close to the Sun's gravitational field on the way to the Earth. Scientists tried experiments which proved this to be true way back in 1919. This was done by taking photographs of the stars during a total eclipse of the Sun, and then photographing the locations of the same stars at night. By comparison of the photographs it was found that Einstein was correct. This was a revelation at that time.

What this means is that light does not travel in a straight line; a light beam is curved. The extent to which it is curved all depends upon how much mass-energy lies in or near its path. We are told that space is boundless but not infinite, and that a beam of light travelling a long time, too long to be practical, would return to its starting point. We do not notice any of this in everyday living, but it is well to know that we live in a very strange world where things are not always what they seem.

Let us turn now from the realm of wide open spaces to the microspace within the atom. Within the atoms of which matter is believed to consist there are sparsely-occupied space regions. The atom is believed to put nearly all of its weight into a nucleus which occupies practically none of its space, while putting practically none of its weight into the electrons which spread out over all of the space. It is hard to realize that because of this structure of matter, a desk top, a railroad track, we ourselves, are mostly space. To approximate a picture of the emptiness of an atom, one might picture the largest building he knows, such as a large cathedral, hollowed out to an empty shell. Begin with nothing in the shell. Then put one housefly in the center for a nucleus. Divide all the rest of the space among from one to 103 tiny specks of dust representing electrons. Such is the emptiness of matter. In the above discussion, there has been no mention of "empty" space. There is no empty space. All space is occupied by something, if only a gravitational field or a faint glimmer of star shine. It is indeed a strange world in which we live.

Since our concept of space is based on our sense perceptions, many concepts of space are possible. These may be subdivided into two types of abstractions: Public space, and private space. Private space may be further subdivided into a separate concept of space for each of our sense perceptions. Private space may be still further subdivided into something absolutely unique for each individual, since each sense perception is filtered through a temperament and interpreted in light of an experience pattern which is unique.

Private space is quite imperfect. It is not the same in all directions, it is of uncertain dimensions, and it is discontinuous. For example, my visual space is that which I can see with my eyes from where I sit. It does not exist behind me at all, unless I turn my head. In each eye there is a blind spot, making a black hole in the private space ahead of me. Olfactory space is what I can detect with my sense of smell. I may detect the aroma of dinner cooking in the kitchen, or the odor of the neighbor's house being painted, or the fresh clean smell of a new snowfall, but my olfactory space does not extend very far. I cannot smell Bagdad or Bombay, or even the stockyards of Chicago from where I sit.

Auditory space is what I can hear with my ears, which might be the sound of children's voices in the school yard nearby, the whistle of a distant train, a plane passing overhead, the dog barking at the postman. I cannot hear the sound of Big Ben striking, nor the soft wash of the waves on a beach in Tasmania.

My gustatory space is still more limited, because I am not an anteater and cannot extend my tongue very far. And my tactile space, chiefly that which I can reach and feel with the skin of my fingers without moving about, is also very local in nature. And there is a portion of my back which does not exist as part of my tactile space, because I cannot reach it. If it itches, it must be scratched by somebody else in whose private space it happens to be at the time.

The list could no doubt be extended. Since we have a sense of gravitational field, the sense which allows a tossed cat always to land on its feet, there must be some kind of private space for that sense too. There are separate sense perceptions for heat, cold, and pain; and probably many other special senses, each of which would theoretically create its own concept of private space. Two forms of private space, visual and auditory, can be most fantastically extended by the movies, radio, and television, especially by the marvelous development of audio-visual magnetic tape. There have been attempts to create movies with extensions of olfactory space, the so-called "smellies." Possibly some day all of the senses will be extended electronically, to simulate total experiences artificially.

Public space has all the virtues which private space lacks. Public space is the same in all directions; it is continuous, perfect, and boundless. It has no blind spots or other limitations. It is the concept of space we use in order to have meetings, go to classes in school, travel in public conveyances, go to the polls to vote, attend church, and do countless other of our everyday activities. It is the space of "togetherness." But it is perfect only because it is a mental abstraction, a psychologic assumption, invented and mutually agreed upon for purposes of social convenience. One does not mention his private space to others; he pretends that he lives in public space. Sanity consists in sharing the same hallucinations in common. Scientists too use public space. However, physical scientists lend added dignity to the concept of public space by calling it <u>physical space</u>. It is this concept of space which scientists use in describing the behavior of the physical world.

Questions

1. What is meant by the scientists' concept of space?
2. How does this relate to the word space as used in the news?
3. Give some examples of space metaphors not found in this book.
4. What is meant by Euclidean space; is it actual space?
5. How did scientists first demonstrate the curvature of space?
6. Explain why there is no such thing as "empty" space.
7. Explain how our concept of space is based on sense perceptions.
8. Explain the difference between public space and private space.
9. Do you believe physical space is a psychologic assumption?
10. What is a light year?

Chapter 4 The Concept of Time

"Time and tide wait for no man," an old proverb goes. By looking in a dictionary we find that "tide" is Anglo-Saxon for time. This leads one to suspect that an early concept of time arose from the rhythmic rising and falling of the sea. The early merchants and shopkeepers had measuring lines and measures of capacity, which they used in selling their wares. Thus they dealt directly with space. Curiously, time was first the prerogative of the priesthood. The early Egyptian priests, who did the writing (hierglyph means priest-write) measured time with sundials and clepsydras. In the western world, mechanical timepieces were used in churches and monasteries by the end of the tenth century, but they were not household items.

In those days the monk who rang the bell which regulated life within the monastery also regulated the life outside its walls. The economic and social life of the village was timed by the church bells. Much later, when mechanical timepieces were sold to the public, people remembered about the bells, for they called their timepieces bells. The word clock merely means bell, in a number of different languages. In French, it is la cloche; and in German, it is die Glocke.

Originally, time measurement depended primarily upon the rotation of the Earth about its axis, and the revolution of the Earth about the Sun. This is still true to a large extent. Short periods of time are measured by an arbitrary unit called the second, defined at present in terms of the cesium clock. Long periods are measured in years. The reference is some great historic epoch, which differs in different parts of the world. In the United States and many other countries, this great epoch is the birth of Christ. For this reason our historical time is divided into that before Christ, or B. C. , and that after, designated as A. D. , in Latin, Anno Domini, which means in the year of our Lord.

The Jews began the day at sunset, hence we find Biblical references to the second hour of the night, etc. An hour was a variable length of time depending upon the season; it was one-twelfth of the period between sunrise and sunset. The expressions "sunrise" and "sunset," which we still use today, show that in our thinking we still regard the earth as standing still while the sun revolves around it, although we know better. In like manner we say "the sun went behind a cloud," when most likely it was a cloud which came under the sun.

Christian church services were divided into seven canonical hours, and the service held at the ninth hour was called nones. This is where we get our word noon. Of course it would not usually be at what we now call twelve o'clock. The twelve o'clock noon, when the sun is at the highest point (meridian) apparently began with seafaring men. Ocean navigators were accustomed to "shooting the sun" at that time to learn their location, and that is when they began the day. Now, for practical reasons on land, we begin the day at midnight instead of at noon.

Let us go back once again to the man in the cave a very long time ago, perceiving a spider on the wall. The man picks up a stick, pokes at the spider, and the spider is frightened and runs away. The man sees the spider move. Suddenly as a consequence something happens within the man's brain. Let us suppose nothing like this had happened in a human brain before. The man perceives the spider now here, now here, now here, now here, in a sequence of locations in space, one after the other. At that moment, he has invented the concept of time. For our word-symbol time merely stands for our ability to perceive events one after another.

If man had never perceived motion, no concept of time could have developed. The key is in the meaning of the word event. It comes from Latin e, meaning out, and venire, meaning to come. To come out; to happen. It seems likely that the human mind takes a sequence of moments, each of which is independent, and puts them together like beads on a string, to create a sense of time. For those who may be familiar with the branch of mathematics known as the calculus, this procedure is the well-known summation of the infinitesimal differentials, "dt." It is a process of taking pieces of time so tiny as to be infinitesimal, and adding an infinite number of them together to get a finite interval of time.

Our sense of time is full of possibilities for wonderful illusions. Some examples will make this concept of time clear. First of all, a movie film consists only of a long string of still photographs. These are photographs of moments, perhaps only one-fiftieth of a second, for instance. But when these moments are projected on a screen in their proper sequence in rapid succession, the mind receives this sensation called motion, the passage of time Nothing actually moves, it is only an illusion. If the film is run backward, time goes in the other direction; as we watch everything which had been done become undone.

Television provides another example of the illusion of time. At the rear of a picture tube, a hot element sends out an intense beam of electron waves, focused on a tiny spot of the fluorescent screen facing the viewer. Electrons are negatively-charged, hence are attracted to a positive charge and repelled from a negative charge. Deflection currents in electromagnetic coils are used to deflect this electron beam, causing it to bend like the stream of water from a garden hose in a strong wind. As a result the bright spot scans very rapidly over the entire face of the picture tube. At the same time, the intensity of the electron beam is automatically modulated to give a pattern of light and shadow. At any one moment there is only one tiny spot of light in one location in space on the television screen. It is our minds which string these spots of light together into the tapestry of continuous motion.

The tape recorder provides a third illustration of our concept of time. On a tape recorder, a roll of plastic tape coated with tiny bits of iron oxide passes over an electromagnetic head, where the fluctuating magnetic field imparts a magnetic pattern in the bits of iron oxide. Watching a tape recorder when it is "recording", one beholds the future rolling toward the head, spending its "moment" at the head, and then immediately rolling on into the past, where it is stored. Moments of both sight and sound, as well as almost any other kind of information, can thus be stored and played back. The relation to our concept of time is obvious.

It is said that pain brings one closer to an understanding of the nature of our concept of time. Certain persons have developed the capacity to endure pain which would be unbearable to the ordinary person. They explain this ability by attributing suffering to the same mental operation which causes us to string moments together to create time. They say that we combine the pain of the present moment with memory of past pain and fear of future pain, and that is why the suffering is unbearable.

It seems intuitive to most persons that there is some aspect of reality which is beyond time, or outside of time. St. Paul expressed this idea in speaking of a material world versus a spiritual world as "things temporal" and "things eternal." It is interesting that much the same idea appears in classical thermodynamics. It has been said that there are three branches of natural science which stand out for their perfection and completeness. These are mechanics, electromagnetics, and thermodynamics. Thermodynamics deals in very pertinent ways with space, matter, and energy; but it does this without even acknowledging that there is such a thing as "time." In the words of the scientist, time simply is not a parameter in classical thermodynamics, which means that time does not appear in its mathematical equations.

Every advance in travel speed causes a new dilemma concerning the measurement of time. When the railroads were built across the United States, each town kept its own time, set more or less by the Sun or by the local jeweler. Each railroad operated on its own time, independently of the others. At one time, six different railways coming into the same city had six different times. Obviously nobody could ever plan to make connections from one train to another.

It was because of the railroads that time came to be standardized in time zones all around the world. First, five time zones were set up across Canada and the United States. Beginning at the east and working westward with each time zone one hour earlier than the one before, these were named Atlantic Standard Time, Eastern Standard Time, Central Standard Time, Mountain Standard Time, and Pacific Standard Time. This is the system we use today. It is a compromise, because it follows the Sun around the Earth in one-hour jerks. But it brought order out of chaos. It was first put into operation at noon on 18 November 1883, and it worked so well that the next year the rest of the world adopted the plan, using the time at Greenwich Observatory in England as the reference.

Few of us realize the extent to which the railroads influenced our thinking in this respect. To quote from Jacques Barzun:

"The railroad was the first great embodiment of modern organization--that prophetic coordination of space, time, matter and men which we now consider the most natural thing in the world. We take it for granted that life will run on schedule; we are sure there is a timetable for everything, a name and number for every object, a supreme regularity and uniformity on which we can rely for the easy pursuit of our urgent purpose and imperious desire. We go to the proper place, ask 'information,' and buy our ticket. Nothing is more simple, regular, universal. Indeed, when Dostoevski wanted to express one of his characters' revolt against the universe (in The Brothers Karamazov), he made the man say that he 'wanted to give back his ticket.'" *

This has worked well for nearly eighty years, but it is beginning to cause confusion as travel rate becomes faster. Travelling by plane, one may find himself missing meals because it is not meal-time, or he may find himself eating lunch at three a.m. It is possible to have breakfast in New York, and breakfast again the same day in San Francisco. It is even possible to travel fast enough to have lunch in New York and breakfast in San Francisco the same day. When Glenn rode the Friendship 7 space craft on 20 February 1962, he watched the sun set four times the same "day," meanwhile

*Reprinted by special permission from Holiday, copyright 1960, by the Curtis Publishing Company.

shuttling back and forth between Tuesdays and Wednesdays. Obviously the time zones which served well for steamship and railroad travel are becoming obsolete for fast air or space travel.

Most of us get our time from electric clocks, of which even the cheapest when plugged into the nearest wall outlet operates at the command of a nationwide 60-cycle alternating current hookup, checked hourly against Naval Observatory time.

Because of the finite time required for transmission of light, radio waves, and electric current (all about the speed of light, which of course varies in different media), there is no simultaneity of time in different locations. The question, what time is it now on the moon? is rather meaningless. This will become important soon when men travel to the moon. Imagine a set of clocks, distributed across the United States, and all wired to a master clock in New York, which can set their time by an electric signal. At a given moment, the master clock sets all the clocks to read exactly "on the hour." But this will be different for each location, by the amount of time required for the signal to reach that location.

This time lag might be insignificant for the span of a continent, but let us now suppose they are also connected to a clock on a planet in the planetary system of the North Star. It would take the signal over 600 years to get there! Anyone looking at the North Star at night sees light which began travelling to the earth shortly before the birth of Marco Polo. As a matter of fact, everything we observe is in the past. Even the light from a friend's face across the table takes a finite time to reach the eye, so that one really observes this friend in the past!

For the needs of science, time measurement is being split finer and finer. All instruments for precise measurement of time use a vibrating body of some sort. Thousands of piezoelectric quartz crystals are in use, timing such things as the frequencies assigned to radio transmitters. At the present time, the most precise clock in use is the cesium clock. Cesium is a metal, element number 55. A cesium crystal placed in an electric field is said to vibrate

9,192,631,770 times a second. Consequently it divides a second into that many parts, and the definition of a second would be the time required for a cesium crystal to vibrate the above number of times. A cesium clock varies less than one second in one thousand years. This kind of time keeping is needed for the Space Age.

Einstein introduced his special relativity theory in 1905. Forty years later, as a result of the success of the "atom" bomb, everyone who understood the significance of this event accepted the part of the theory which reduces mass and energy to the same thing. The equation $E = mc^2$ is now known to all. It has been observed in large letters on a banner above the pulpit of an evangelist; and it has become a symbol of the Science Cult. It makes no difference that most of these people have no clear idea of what it means.

Other parts of the special relativity theory say that mass increases with speed, length shortens in the direction of motion, and time slows down as mass increases or as speed increases. None of these effects have any noticeable influence on the affairs of everyday life, including space travel such as that of John Glenn in the Friendship 7 space vehicle. This space craft travelled at 17,500 miles per hour, about five miles per second, which is only three-thousandths of one percent of the speed of light. This was not fast enough to make any noticeable difference as observed from Earth stations.

Nevertheless, the special relativity theory has been proved true experimentally using small particles in motion. Electrons accelerated in a cyclotron increase in mass. Mesons from cosmic rays, which one would not expect to exist long enough to strike the Earth, actually do strike the Earth, presumably because their time has been slowed down due to rapid motion. The slower time on the Sun due to its very high mass-energy field results in a red shift in its spectrum, indicating that the electrons in its atoms are moving more slowly than they would on the Earth. The blue glow seen in the water of a swimming pool type nuclear reactor is due to electrons travelling through water faster than the speed of light, thus piling up light ahead of them just as planes at Mach 1 pile up sound waves. The author realizes that he has used words in this paragraph which have not been defined. To go into the subject more thoroughly, however, would carry us too far into science.

If an electron is thought of as a sphere at rest, as its motion increases it will become more like a pumpkin, flattening in the direction of motion until at the speed of light it should be a flat disc of zero thickness. One's wrist watch should run a little faster on top of Pike's Peak than in Death Valley. The Spanish surrealist painter Salvadore Dali depicted ideas about relativity in his paintings showing watches hanging over tree limbs, melting and dripping in the hot sun.

Since each body of matter (mass-energy) has its own time rate, which time is real? If the length of an arrow depends upon how fast it is shot through the air, what is its real length? If the mass of a substance increases with speed relative to a reference point, what is its real mass? These questions are asked in order to give examples of a type of question which has no meaning in science.

The equations of relativity merely describe observed behavior of the physical world. If this behavior, which we do not observe in our everyday life, seems odd and unbelievable, it is only because we put too much trust in what is "obvious" to us, and rely too much upon our sense perceptions and intuition, which tend to mislead us at every turn.

The non-scientist must be on his guard against persons who take theories of physical science and apply them where they do not belong, have nothing to say, and become ridiculous. For instance, the statement is sometimes read, "relativity theory says that everything is relative: thus moral values are relative, and there are no absolute moral standards of human behavior." This extrapolation is unjustified.

Each person has his own private time. Private time moves slowly when one is young, and more rapidly as one grows older. Each year in one's life seems to go by a little faster than the year before. Presumably this is because each succeeding year is a smaller portion of one's total experience. To a baby one year old, a year seems like a whole lifetime, because it is. To an eighty year old, a year is only a little more than one percent of a lifetime. If one can imagine a life after death, in which experience goes on and on, a man who had lived a million years might find the years going past like minutes.

There is another way in which private time varies. It passes rapidly when one is engrossed, and lags when one is bored. Many bored persons must try to invent ways to "kill" time. Pleasant sport or entertainment is called "pastime" because it helps make time pass. It seems strange that although time is what each person has the least of, and Queen Elizabeth in her last moments offered all her possessions for an extra moment of time, millions of persons have "time on their hands." Time seems to fly when one is on vacation, but when forced to listen to a long-winded speaker, time seems to crawl. And in a great crisis, it seems that "time stands still."

The mind has a built-in vibration in the brain waves, oscillations in microvoltage which are constantly produced in the brain so long as one is alive. These can be measured by means of an instrument called the electroencephalograph. The normal alpha-waves average ten waves per second. But the frequency of the various brain waves can vary from about three to one hundred per second. Probably these brain waves are responsible for some of our sense of time, although perhaps not on a very reliable basis. The heart beat is another time counting machine and it too can fluctuate widely. Private time cannot be relied upon.

Out of necessity and for social convenience, man has invented a purely mental construct or psychologic abstraction known as public time. This is an arbitrary time, kept by machinery, the various kinds of clocks etc. It is public time that enables one to catch a train or plane, to arrange to meet someone at a certain time and place two years hence. to attend classes, and in general to order one's life. Scientists also use public time in their experiments, but they call it physical time. It is in terms of physical time, along with physical space previously discussed, that scientists must describe the behavior of the physical world, which is the task of science.

As a matter of fact, in describing such behavior it is not possible to separate time from space. They constitute the concept of a space-time continuum, within the fabric of which all events in the physical world are placed. Because space is represented by three dimensions, time is often called the fourth dimension. A person living in a world of two dimensions would not be able to comprehend a third dimension, because he could not get outside and look at it; since we live in three dimensions, we are not able to get outside and look at it, so we interpret a fourth dimension as being a sequence of three dimensions in a time sequence.

Time is sometimes defined as that which passes while entropy increases. This idea will be discussed in the chapter on energy.

In summary, we have seen that both "space" and "time" are words used by scientists as symbols to stand for certain mental concepts. In the chapters to follow we shall learn that matter and energy also are mental concepts, and that in the last analysis energy in its various forms seems to be the only physical reality. Theories of space, time, matter, and energy are at present in a state of change. The neat and orderly simplicity of the nineteenth century is gone, and with it the assurance that one can correctly say that matter and energy exist in time and space. It seems very likely that the truth may be the other way round: that time and space exist only because of matter and energy. We shall not attempt to solve the problem here, but shall only point out this possibility.

Questions

1. Why is everything and everyone we see in the past?
2. Why is time called the fourth dimension?
3. How is the second defined in terms of the cesium clock?
4. What does the word "clock" mean?
5. What is meant by the "concept" of time?
6. How did railroads influence our thinking about time?

7. Discuss the meaninglessness of simultaneity of time.
8. Discuss the relativity of time.
9. How does private time differ from public time?
10. Have you ever experienced the feeling that time "stood still?"

Chapter 5 Structure of the Atom

We come now to the third concept of science--the concept of matter. Matter is the "substance" of the physical world around us. Traditionally, matter is defined as that which occupies space and has mass. Mass is a measure of the quantity of matter in a body. It is what causes inertia--the resistance to change in motion. The terms mass and energy are just two ways of expressing the same thing. We shall go into this when we come to the concept of energy. Weight is due to the pull of gravity on mass, and usually we think of mass in terms of weight. For instance, in chemistry it has been the custom to refer to the atomic "weights" of the elements, and when mass is determined on a balance, the operation is called "weighing." We are inconsistent in this regard, because we also refer to "the law of conservation of mass." It may be that eventually we shall overcome this habit and speak of atomic mass and molecular mass. We may even speak of weighing as "massing." This would be better, because under most practical conditions the mass of a body is constant, not being dependent upon a gravitational field.

It is intuitive to believe that matter comes in tiny pieces; anthropologists who have questioned very young children and primitive tribes find this to be the case. These tiny pieces of matter correspond to our concept of atoms and molecules. The Greeks had such a notion, and the word atom comes from a Greek word atomos, which means "cannot be split." Even though scientists have split the atom into smaller particles, we go right on calling them atoms just the same. The story of matter is the story of the elements of which matter is composed. The early idea was that there were only four elements; earth, fire, air, and water. The present idea is that there are many elements, over one hundred, although most of us never encounter more than about one half of this number. The atom may be defined as the simplest particle of an element. Modern atomic theory does not go back to the atomism of Greek philosophy. It begins with the theory of an English chemist named Dalton, who first formulated rules of chemical atomic theory about 1803 A. D.

The present idea is, then, that all matter is composed of elements, all elements are composed of atoms, and all atoms are composed of certain fundamental particles. More than a hundred years ago it was observed that an electric current does not flow smoothly and continuously, but passes through a conductor in pulsating jerks, all of which are exactly alike. Each of these individual units of electricity was assigned the name, electron, and was described as being a unit of negative electricity, or negative charge. The electron is one of the fundamental particles of matter.

This is one of the difficult places in science, because it involves words such as electricity, charge, and fundamental, which are really just labels pinned on observations we do not understand too well. Electricity, for instance, is merely a word-symbol standing for an observed behavior of matter resulting from that matter having a charge. And we don't really know what charge means either, excepting to say that there are two different kinds of charge, which attract each other, although two charges of the same kind repel each other. All of this is based upon observed behavior of matter, and not on theory. Fundamental is another word which is used all the time but is difficult to define. When a science teacher uses the word fundamental, what he usually means by this word is "Don't ask me any more about it, I don't know either."

After the electron was found, another fundamental particle within the atom was discovered, having about the same mass as a hydrogen atom, but having a charge opposite to the charge of the electron. Since the charge on the electron was arbitrarily assigned a "negative" charge, the new particle was arbitrarily said to have a "positive" charge, and it was named a proton. It must be understood that these opposite charges could just as well have been given other names, such as A and B, or John and Mary, or unused names such as gloop and mulg. It is very unfortunate that the words positive and negative were chosen, because these two words have other connotations in their own right. To make matters worse, the symbols chosen to stand for positive was +, and for negative -. Now it happens that these are arithmetic symbols for plus and minus, meaning add or subtract. Here they have no such meaning, and this is a source of endless confusion for the beginning student.

After the electron and proton were discovered, another particle was found with a mass similar to that of the proton but without a charge. Being neutral, it was named the neutron. These three, the electrons, protons, and neutrons, are the fundamental particles of which all matter is made. To go into the detailed evidence out of which grew the present concepts of these particles, or to discuss certain other particles postulated in modern physics, would carry us too far for the purpose of this book.

It is natural for man to be curious about how these elements came to exist. By whatever means this came about, it is the story of Creation, an act of bringing the Universe into existence out of nothing. Scientists generally do not attempt to go very far into the mystery which confronts us here (there is mystery in science too), but when they do they generally find themselves not much farther along than "In the beginning God created."

However, scientists do speculate about the origin and relative abundance of the elements found in nature. One such theory of cosmogony holds that if at some definite point in time and space, billions of years ago, a vast swarm of neutrons suddenly appeared, then it would be possible to imagine how all the rest of the elements resulted, how the stars and planets were created, and how man finally came to be. The physicist Gamow, who is one of the leading writers on this subject, summarized the relative difficulty of these accomplishments by saying that it probably took less than an hour to make the atoms, a few hundred million years to make the stars and planets, and at least three billion years to make man. Whatever the implications of these statements for one's personal views, all of this is speculation and its acceptance is not essential as part of the concept of matter.

The basis of this theory of a Creation is the fact that free neutrons are radioactive, with a half-life of about thirteen minutes. Given such a swarm of neutrons, within the thirteen minutes one-half of them would have decomposed, each neutron yielding one proton and one electron. Thus within minutes after the Creation, the Universe would have existed chiefly as a mixture of neutrons, protons, and electrons, and thus would be equipped with the fundamental particles of matter out of which all the elements could then be manufactured. The first one would be hydrogen, since it is the simplest element, with an atom consisting of one proton and one electron. Scientists are encouraged in this postulate by observing that even to this day the Universe consists chiefly of hydrogen; according to some authorities as much as ninety-five percent of it is hydrogen.

Pursuing this idea further, the other elements would have appeared later, and in decreasing quantity with increasing complexity, their atoms being built from hydrogen atoms and free neutrons to form central nuclei, which would finally become surrounded by appropriate numbers of electrons to form atoms of the various elements, and molecules from the various atoms combining together. Thus all elements might conceivably have been built originally from hydrogen units. It is interesting that this idea was put forth by Prout as long ago as 1815 A. D. By observing that the relative masses of the various elements were reasonably-close multiples of the unit mass of a hydrogen atom, he proposed the idea that hydrogen was the primary substance from which all other elements had been formed. His hypothesis was soon discarded, only to be brought back to life in recent times. It has imperfections, but at the present time one may say that it is difficult to accept Prout's hypothesis or not accept it.

Carrying this idea of the Creation a bit further, as time went on the atoms would have joined together wherever possible to form molecules. A molecule is the simplest unit of a compound, just as an atom is the simplest unit of an element. A compound is not like a mixture; every molecule of a compound always contains atoms in combining ratios of simple whole numbers (1, 2, 3, etc.) and hence in definite proportions by mass. They are united to each other by chem ical bonds which we shall describe later, and they cannot be separated by ordinary mechanical means such as tweezers, like one can separate a mixture of salt and pepper. The process by which a compound is formed from its elements is called a chemical reaction. A compound is a distinct substance, formed by reaction of two or more elements in definite proportions by mass (weight).

Before going into the structure of a compound, we must first go into the structure of the atom. Each atom is believed to have two parts:

1. A central, positively-charged nucleus. Its positive charge is due to the presence of protons. An element may be defined as a substance, all atoms of which contain the same number of protons in the nucleus. The number of protons in the nucleus is called the atomic number. An element may also have neutrons in its nucleus. These neutrons, if present, contribute to its mass but not to its charge. Neutrons are sometimes called the "nuclear glue" which holds the protons together in the nucleus. If a neutron loses an electron, it becomes a proton; at the same time, one of the protons will receive the electron and become a neutron. An analogy might be two cooks in a kitchen baking potatoes. One cook takes a potato out of the oven, but it is too hot to hold so he tosses it to the other cook, who in turn quickly tosses it back, etc. Since the rules of the game forbid setting the potato down or dropping it on the floor, the two cooks need each other in order to handle this hot potato.

For practical purposes, the total mass of the protons and neutrons in a nucleus of an atom is its atomic mass (atomic weight), since the electrons weigh only about 1/1845th as much as a neutron and proton). Some atoms have the same number of protons, but different numbers of neutrons, and these atoms of the same element are called <u>isotopes</u>.

2. There is a negatively-charged region surrounding the nucleus. The negative charge is due to one or more

electrons, the fundamental and discrete units of negative charge, all of which are exactly alike. An atom is electrically-neutral, hence the number of electrons equals the number of protons. If an atom gains or loses one or more electrons, it becomes an ion, to be discussed later.

Chemistry may be defined as the study of changes in the number and arrangement of the electrons surrounding the nuclei of the various atoms. All of the chemical reactions involve these electron changes. For this reason, the study of chemistry is largely a study of what happens to the electrons. Although the border between chemistry and physics is becoming more and more blurred, there is a distinction between a chemical change and a physical change. A physical change may be defined as a change in properties of a substance without a change in chemical composition. A property is defined as the behavior of a substance as measured by instruments, remembering that the sense organs such as the eyes, are instruments. When ice melts, it is a physical change. Matter is known to exist in three forms, known as phases. The three phases of matter are solid, liquid, and gas. Ice, liquid water, and water vapor are the three phases of water. Chemically they are identical, but they differ in physical structure and properties.

As a result of recent success in methods of releasing energy from the nucleus of the atom, a relatively new and rapidly growing field of physical science has appeared. This new science is generally known as nuclear physics. It is concerned with changes within the nucleus of the atom. We shall mention this later in the section on the concept of energy.

From mathematical calculations, scientists have imagined how the electrons are arranged in the space about the nucleus of the atom. This arrangement concept has resulted from what is known as quantum theory, a quite advanced kind of mathematics. It is important to emphasize that the mental pictures of atoms are imaginary. One is not entitled to say "this is how the atom is." All we are entitled to say is, "This is our mental concept of the atom." One might call some of the pictures that result "mathematical" models, as distinguished from the former "mechanical" models which are no longer tenable.

It is not necessary to be able to read the language of mathematics to grasp the essence of quantum theory as it applies to the atom. We can illustrate this by the vibrations of a string on a guitar. If the string is plucked, a wave motion will be set up, and a musical tone will be heard. Because the string is fastened at both ends, this boundary condition limits the string to certain vibrations; no others are possible. Thus the string may vibrate (Fig. 1) as a whole (a), in two parts with a stationary node in the middle (b), in three parts (c), etc. However, there is no possibility of the string vibrating in just any or all ways.

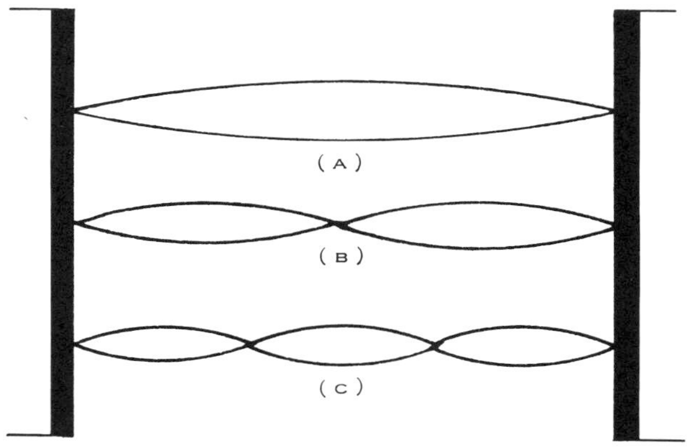

FIG. 1. DIAGRAM ILLUSTRATING QUANTIZED VIBRATIONS OF A STRING FASTENED AT EACH END.

As another example, a bugle can sound only certain tones, the tones used for bugle calls. It cannot produce the musical tones in between. A bugler cannot slide from one tone to the other like the player on a trombone can do. In ballroom dancing, the couples are more or less free to move about the ballroom; but in square dancing, the couples are arranged in sets of four couples facing each other, and their motions are limited to their own particular set and its floor space. These are examples from everyday life of situations which in the language of the scientist are referred to as being "quantized."

According to quantum theory, the electrons which surround the nucleus of an atom can exist only at certain energy levels, called quantum levels. These energy levels may be thought of as concentric spherical shells surrounding the nucleus. Each shell describes the average distance from the nucleus to the electrons in that shell.

The closer an electron lies to the nucleus, the less the energy it contains. For this reason electrons will ordinarily try to be as close to the nucleus as possible, just as water poured into a bucket fills it from the bottom up and not from the top down. However, if sufficient energy is put into an atom, it will force electrons to move into shells with higher energy content. The electron then is in an excited state. In passing from a lower energy level to a higher energy level, the electron cannot exist at any energy level in between. In other words, the electron passes from one energy level to another in zero time.

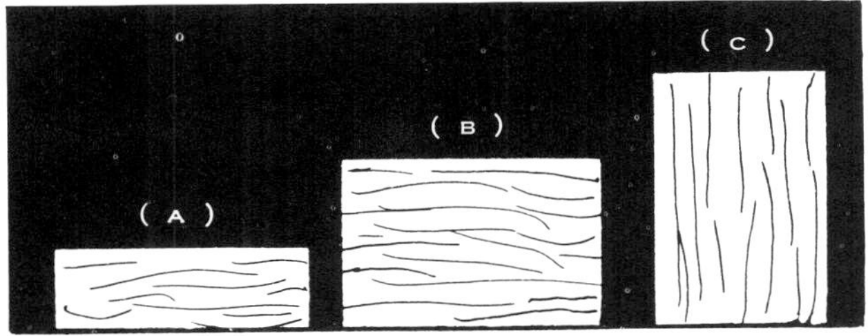

FIG. 2. DIAGRAM OF A WOOD BLOCK ILLUSTRATING QUANTIZED ENERGY LEVELS.

This principle can be illustrated with a block of wood 2 X 4 X 6 inches (Fig. 2). The lowest energy level, called the ground state of an atom, is illustrated by the block lying in position (a). The next higher energy level is position (b), and the highest energy level is position (c). The block can not be placed in any positions other than these. Just where the ground state is will depend upon whether the block is placed on a table, or on the floor.

The concentric spherical shells representing energy levels about the nucleus of an atom are designated by numbers, counting out from the nucleus: 1, 2, 3, 4, etc. They are also designated by letters: K, L, M, N, etc. Within the energy levels are sublevels known as orbitals (not orbits), which describe how the electrons are believed to be arranged in three-dimensional space according to mathematical calculations. These orbitals outline zones of probability of electron density, that is, places where it is most probable that each electron will be found. The shapes of the orbitals (they are solid shapes and not flat diagrams as they usually appear to be on paper) are not arbitrary; they are derived from mathematical wave equations which tell the probability of finding an electron in a particular place. Actually, there is a certain probability of a given electron being anywhere in the Universe, but the probability drops off rapidly beyond a fixed region near the nucleus. These orbital shapes tell us where the electrons are most likely to be most of the time. A wave equation cannot tell where an electron is, or how fast it is moving, both at the same time. This is known as the Heisenberg uncertainty principle.

In the atoms we shall consider, we shall be concerned with only two types of orbitals, known as "s" and "p" orbitals. The s orbitals are spherical in shape, there is one in each energy level, and it can hold two electrons. The nucleus is in the center of the s orbitals. There are three p orbitals. They are dumbbell shaped and each is at right angles to the other two. Together the three p orbitals can hold as many as six electrons. There are no p orbitals in the first energy level.

Let us consider the hydrogen atom, since it is the simplest atom. Instead of thinking of the electron as travelling in a circular orbit around the nucleus, as it is often incorrectly pictured, it is better to think of the electron as travelling in a wave-like motion, in and out around the nucleus, so that it occupies the entire space in the ball-shaped region known as the 1 s (pronounced one-ess) orbital. Sometimes this is pictured as an electron "cloud" surrounding the nucleus. All attempts fail because it is something we really are not able to think about. Most of the mass of an atom is in its nucleus, but the electrons occupy most of the space. If an atom were enlarged to the size of a basketball, there would still be nothing large enough to see.

Scientists, and the technologists who put their findings to work, have accepted the modern concept of the atom because these atoms with their electron orbitals make chemistry much clearer. It is in much better agreement with experimental observations than older theories. And the accomplishments made possible by accepting this concept have been very gratifying. Those who are not scientists will also find that this concept of the structure of matter, based upon what is now called electron configuration, makes chemistry much more understandable. One need not even concern himself about whether or not the concept is correct; the concept works, wherever it is applied, better than anything which has been known before, and this alone is sufficient reason for accepting it until something better replaces it.

Each orbital can hold one, but not more than two, electrons. When it holds two electrons, these electrons must be of opposite "spin." Since an electron in motion is an electric current (that is all that electric current is), this spin results in a magnetic field. Most atoms are not attracted to a magnet, and hence are said to be diamagnetic. This is because all their electrons are paired, so that the magnetism caused by each cancels out the opposite magnetism caused by its mate. However, there are some atoms which have odd electrons, that is, electrons which are not paired, and these substances then are attracted by a magnet. Iron is an example. In everyday language such substances are said to be magnetic, but the scientist calls them paramagnetic.

One can predict where the electrons will be in the various orbitals, using the rule that electrons fill the lowest energy levels first, and knowing the number of electrons in the atom in question from the atomic number of that element.

The electron configurations for the first eighteen elements are shown in Table 1. It should be noted that the lack of a superscript indicates that only one electron is present in that orbital. The superscript ^{2}, as in the electron configuration of helium, which is $1s^2$, does not read "square," but means that there are two electrons in the 1S orbital. It will be noted that in each case the sum of the superscripts adds up to the atomic number. The electrons in the outer shell, to the right of the vertical line, are called the valence electrons. The importance of being able to write the electron configuration from the atomic number, is to be able to find

TABLE 1. ELECTRON CONFIGURATION

Name of Element	Symbol	Atomic No.	Electron Configuration
hydrogen	H	1	1s
helium	He	2	$1s^2$
lithium	Li	3	$1s^2$ 2s
beryllium	Be	4	$1s^2$ $2s^2$
boron	B	5	$1s^2$ $2s^2$ 2p
carbon	C	6	$1s^2$ $2s^2$ $2p^2$
nitrogen	N	7	$1s^2$ $2s^2$ $2p^3$
oxygen	O	8	$1s^2$ $2s^2$ $2p^4$
fluorine	F	9	$1s^2$ $2s^2$ $2p^5$
neon	Ne	10	$1s^2$ $2s^2$ $2p^6$
sodium	Na	11	$1s^2$ $2s^2$ $2p^6$ 3s
magnesium	Mg	12	$1s^2$ $2s^2$ $2p^6$ $3s^2$
aluminum	Al	13	$1s^2$ $2s^2$ $2p^6$ $3s^2$ 3p
silicon	Si	14	$1s^2$ $2s^2$ $2p^6$ $3s^2$ $3p^2$
phosphorus	P	15	$1s^2$ $2s^2$ $2p^6$ $3s^2$ $3p^3$
sulfur	S	16	$1s^2$ $2s^2$ $2p^6$ $3s^2$ $3p^4$
chlorine	Cl	17	$1s^2$ $2s^2$ $2p^6$ $3s^2$ $3p^5$
argon	Ar	18	$1s^2$ $2s^2$ $2p^6$ $3s^2$ $3p^6$

TABLE 2. PERIODIC TABLE OF THE ELEMENTS SIMPLIFIED

PERIOD:		GROUP 1	2	3	4	5	6	7	8
1	Electrons in 1st shell	H 1							He 2
2	Electrons in 1st shell 2nd shell	Li 2 1	Be 2 2	B 2 3	C 2 4	N 2 5	O 2 6	F 2 7	Ne 2 8
3	Electrons in 1st shell 2nd shell 3rd shell	Na 2 8 1	Mg 2 8 2	Al 2 8 3	Si 2 8 4	P 2 8 5	S 2 8 6	Cl 2 8 7	Ar 2 8 8
4	Electrons in 1st shell 2nd shell 3rd shell 4th shell	K 2 8 8 1	Ca 2 8 8 2	....				Br 2 8 18 7	Kr 2 8 18 8
5	Electrons in 1st shell 2nd shell 3rd shell 4th shell 5th shell	Rb 2 8 18 8 1	Sr 2 8 18 8 2	....				I 2 8 18 18 7	Xe 2 8 18 18 8

Notes: The sum of the numbers under each symbol is the atomic number for that element. Note that the number of electrons in the outer shell is the same as the group number. A number of elements are omitted. A complete periodic table of the elements may be found in any standard textbook of chemistry.

out how many electrons are in this outer shell, because this determines to a large extent the chemical behavior of the element which can then be predicted. For each element, the nucleus and the electrons not in the outer shell are together called the kernel.

There are low points or energy slots in the electron configuration where utmost stability occurs. These occur every time the outer shell builds up to eight electrons. Thus if the elements are lined up in eight groups in the order of their atomic numbers, they fall automatically into groups with a repetitive pattern of behavior which can be predicted. This useful arrangement of the elements is known as the periodic table (Table 2). In such a table, the group numbers across the top indicate the number of electrons in the outer shell, ranging from one to eight. Group eight consists of elements having eight electrons in the outer shell, and since this is the utterly stable arrangement, these elements are not reactive and hence are said to be inert, which means "idle." They are all gases. The outer shell of eight is sometimes called an octet. It is a coincidence that this repetitive pattern by eights is like the musical scale, and the periodic scale is a little like a piano keyboard, where the same tone an octave higher recurs every eighth key. Since these gases are inert, one might be justified in calling all the other elements "ert" elements, but the word ert seems to have disappeared from the vocabulary except in Scotland.

Questions

1. What does the word "atom" mean? Is it appropriate?
2. Did modern atomic theory begin with the Greeks?
3. What is the definition of electricity; of charge; of fundamental?
4. With regard to electric charge, what do "positive" and "negative" mean?
5. Explain the neutron swarm theory of the Creation.

6. Name three fundamental units of matter.

7. What is Prout's hypothesis? Is there any evidence in favor of it?

8. Define element, atom, molecule, and compound.

9. Describe the two parts of an atom.

10. What is an isotope?

11. Define chemistry, and explain how a chemical change differs from a physical change.

12. Explain what is meant by a quantized situation. How does this apply to atomic theory?

13. What is the electron configuration of chlorine?

14. What is the value and significance of the periodic table?

Chapter 6 Bonds and Their Properties

The story is told of a woman in Boston long ago, who when asked if she had ever travelled replied, "But of course not. You see, I am already here." The inert gases are like that. They have no incentive either to gain or lose electrons to achieve the inert gas structure, because they are "already there." All other atoms tend to gain or lose electrons in the outer shell, in order to achieve an electron configuration most nearly resembling that of the nearest inert gas, and this is the driving force which explains the chemical behavior of the elements. It is for this reason alone that knowledge of the electron configuration of the elements, and the information resulting from it which can also be obtained by correct interpretation of the periodic table, is the key to understanding chemical reactions. Incidentally, one inert gas, helium, is unlike the others in that it contains only two electrons.

There are two ways in which an atom can gain or lose electrons to achieve an inert gas structure: (a) by transfer of electrons with the formation of ions, and (b) by sharing of electrons with other atoms to form molecules of compounds.

Let us examine first the simplest example of electron sharing. It will be recalled that a hydrogen atom consists of one proton (the nucleus) and one electron. The proton is in the center and the electron completely surrounds it with an average spherical distance indicated by the configuration **1 s**. However, hydrogen atoms do not exist singly like this under ordinary conditions. Hydrogen gas consists of molecules, each containing two hydrogen atoms. Obviously the hydrogen atoms are happier going around in pairs this way; they feel more relaxed. There is less tension; the scientific term for it is less energy content. Every system always tries to do whatever is possible to get to a lower energy level. That is why water runs down hill, and clock springs unwind.

The electron configuration of the nearest inert gas, helium, is $1\ s^2$. The nearest approach to this configuration is achieved when two atoms of hydrogen share their two electrons in common. Such an arrangement, in which the mutual sharing together of two electrons by the nuclei of two atoms, hence a "shared electron pair," is called a covalent bond. This is the kind of bond which holds the constituent atoms to each other to form molecules of compounds. Both electrons are attracted to both nuclei, which holds the nuclei close to each other even though they repel each other. At the same time the two electrons repel each other but are attracted to the two positive nuclei. As a matter of fact, the two electrons now occupy a single orbital around both of the nuclei. This is called a molecular orbital. To go further into molecular orbital theory would carry us too far. Hydrogen gas is called a diatomic molecule. To indicate this by means of symbols, its molecular formula is written H_2. Sometimes the analogy is presented of a catamaran sailboat. A single narrow sailboat, like the hydrogen atom, is unstable in the water, but if two of the sailboats are fastened together, a stable sailboat results.

Everyone seems to know this much about chemistry, that "water is H_2O." From practically every standpoint, the most important compound on the Earth is water. Most of the hydrogen on Earth is combined in the form of water. Free hydrogen gas is too light to stay in the Earth's atmosphere and tends to escape into outer space. Even the oxygen which we breathe in the air originally came from water. There is a theory that long ago, when the Earth was enveloped by water vapor, the water vapor in the upper atmosphere decomposed, the lighter hydrogen gas escaping and the heavier oxygen gas settling down to the surface of the Earth. We literally live and breathe at the bottom of a sea of oxygen and other heavy gases (chiefly nitrogen) a mixture called the atmosphere.

Life must have come to the Earth much later than liquid water, since water was the first liquid to appear on Earth capable of supporting life. It seems likely that life began in water. Most forms of life still occupy their watery habitat, and those forms of life which have emerged from water carry their watery environment around with them. All vital chemical reactions take place in water.

By referring to the electron configuration of oxygen, $1s^2 2s^2 2p^4$, we see that oxygen has six electrons in the outer shell. These are the valence electrons. The same information can be obtained by noting that oxygen is in group six of the periodic table. The nearest inert gas is neon, which has ten electrons. Oxygen would need to gain only two more electrons to complete its octet and become similar in configuration to neon. It would not <u>become</u> neon, of course, it would still be oxygen because it would still have eight protons in the nucleus, while neon has ten.

We said that one way to get these extra electrons is by sharing. What happens in the case of water is that two hydrogen atoms come alongside and share their electrons with the oxygen atom, thus producing a molecule of the compound, water. The two electrons shared in common by an oxygen nucleus and a hydrogen nucleus hold them together tightly, and this force is just like that in hydrogen gas, a covalent bond. If we represent the kernel by the symbol for the element (a common practice in chemistry), and indicate the valence electrons by dots, the oxygen atom would be written

$\cdot\ddot{\underset{\cdot}{O}}:$ and the hydrogen atom would be writen $H\cdot$; and putting these together to form a molecule of water we would have

$H\ :\ddot{\underset{\cdot\cdot}{O}}:$. The oxygen now has the eight electrons it desires,
$\quad\ \ H$

and each hydrogen has two, so they are happy. No apology is offered for speaking about atoms in anthropomorphic terms since we are human beings, this is the easiest way to understand. In analogy with the catamaran, the stability of the water molecule could be compared to the stability of a dugout canoe with two outriggers.

We might examine at this time the two elements next below oxygen in atomic number, namely nitrogen and carbon.

From their electron configurations we would be easily led to the formation of similar hydrogen compounds,

```
             ..                              H
        H   :N:   H          and         H  :C:  H
             ..                              ..
             H                               H
```

These are the familiar compounds, ammonia (NH_3), and methane CH_4, natural gas), and they are stable compounds. Only one more compound will be encountered in this book, and that is hydrogen chloride gas, with the electron configuration arrangement H :Cl .

Each of these formulas represents a molecule, hence it has a molecular weight (mass). This is the sum of the atomic weights of all the atoms shown in the formula. In the above examples, the atomic weight of hydrogen is one, of carbon 12, nitrogen, 14, oxygen 16, and chlorine 35. 5. Adding these together, the molecular weights would be: methane 16, ammonia 17, water (vapor) 18, and hydrogen chloride 36. 5. In general, the atomic mass of an element is the sum of the number of neutrons plus protons in its nucleus. The reason chlorine does not have a whole number is that it occurs naturally as a mixture of isotopes.

Atomic weights were formerly based on oxygen as a standard, but beginning in 1961 all atomic weight (atomic mass) values were revised to be based on carbon-12, which means the pure isotope of carbon which contains six protons and six neutrons. The atomic weight (mass) of any element is the weight of the same number of atoms of that element as are contained in 12 weight units of carbon-12. Atomic weights and molecular weights, and in the case of ion mixtures formula weights, are used in chemistry for making quantitative calculations. We shall have no need for them here.

In addition to the method of electron sharing to form covalent bonds, just discussed, atoms can also achieve the inert gas structure by electron transfer. Which method will be used cannot always be predicted, but is determined by laboratory experiments. However, one can generalize to this extent, that atoms at the far left of the periodic table, called metals, have a great urge to lose one or more electrons by transfer, thus becoming positively-charged ions.

And atoms at the far right of the periodic table, called nonmetals, are equally anxious to acquire additional electrons, thus becoming negatively-charged ions. In metals, the electrons are relatively loose, and easily move from atom to atom. They therefore conduct electricity and are called conductors. An electric current is a flow of electrons.

In nonmetals, electrons are relatively tight, and do not so easily move from atom to atom. They do not conduct electricity, and are called insulators. Metals are usually shiny and nonmetals are usually dull. Among the first 18 elements, shown in Table 1, those which tend to lose electrons by transfer are the metals Li, Na, K, Be, Mg, Ca, and Al. Those which readily gain electrons by transfer are F and Cl. The others in between are more likely to share electrons than to transfer.

Our chief example of electron transfer will be the reaction between a sodium atom and a chlorine atom. Sodium metal, in group 1, needs to lose only one electron to become like neon, while chlorine, in group 7, needs to gain one electron to become like argon in electron configuration. When the two get together, they immediately perform this transaction of electron transfer. A sodium atom reacts with a chlorine atom to yield a sodium ion and a chlorine ion. In chemical shorthand, this is written in the form of a reaction equation:

$$Na + Cl \rightarrow Na^{+} + Cl^{-}$$

The resulting mixture of sodium ions and chlorine ions (chemists call them chlori<u>de</u> ions) is sodium chloride, common table salt, often written simply NaCl. This is not a molecule and hence it does not have any molecular weight, since salts of this sort are not compounds. A salt may be defined as an indefinite but equal number of oppositely-charged ions. The weight of NaCl is called its formula weight. Sodium chloride always consists of this mixture of ions, whether it is dissolved in water or is in the form of dry salt crystals.

Since these ions have opposite charges, they are attracted to each other, since it is fundamental that opposite charges attract. The force of attraction in this case is not a <u>co</u>valent bond. It is called an electrovalent bond, because it is due to the force of electrostatic attraction. The difference between a covalent bond and an electrovalent bond is not always as distinct as in the examples we have chosen, because many covalent bonds also have a certain degree of ionic character.

When salt crystals are placed in water, attraction of the water for the ions (called hydration) is sufficiently forceful to pull the ions apart, so the salt dissolves. In some cases, hydration is not forceful enough to pull the ions apart, and in such cases the salts are insoluble in water. Silver chloride is an example.

One must be careful to avoid confusing atoms with ions. Often they have quite different properties. Thus sodium and chlorine atoms would be poisonous if taken into the body, but sodium and chloride ions are ordinary salt which we sprinkle on our food. In chemistry, there are many ion mixtures belonging to the class known as salts. We could have for instance, lithium chloride, $LiCl$; potassium chloride, KCl; magnesium chloride, $MgCl_2$; and aluminum chloride, $AlCl_3$. All of these have electrovalent bonds. In water solution, salts conduct electricity, hence they are also called electrolytes.

Everyone has personal sense data testifying to the existence of acids, because they are the only substances which taste sour. There are only four tastes, salty, sweet, sour, and bitter. Vinegar was undoubtedly the earliest acid known, and there is reference to it in the earliest literature. Hydrochloric acid occurs in the stomach, and auto batteries contain sulfuric acid. The first base known in early times nitron, which we now call soda, or sodium carbonate. The words "acid" and "base" might never have become part of the chemists' vocabulary if there had always been the knowledge of electron transfer which we know now. An acid may be defined in a completely general way, as any substance which is acting to receive electrons by transfer. When a chlorine atom receives one electron to become a chloride ion, it is acting as an acid, but it does not add anything to our knowledge to label it an acid.

Likewise, the general definition of a base is any substance which is acting to lose electrons. When a sodium atom loses one electron to become a sodium ion, it is acting as a base. All other definitions of acid and base are included in these general definitions. Every chemical reaction is an electrical transaction. An electric current is a movement of electrons. Something always gains electrons and something else always loses electrons, so that electrons go from here to there, an electric current or a flow of electrons. If this does not happen, it is not a chemical reaction but probably only a physical change.

There is another set of terms which came into use before this knowledge of electron transfer-- oxidation and reduction. Oxidation is defined as the act of losing electrons, while reduction is defined as the act of gaining electrons. Thus in a general sense, every chemical reaction is an oxidation-reduction reaction, and also an acid-base reaction.

If hydrogen chloride gas is bubbled into water, a chemical reaction takes place between one molecule of hydrogen chloride and one molecule of water, both of which are true chemical compounds with covalent bonds:

$$HCl \quad + \quad H_2O \quad \rightarrow \quad H_3O^+ \quad + \quad Cl^-$$

The chlorine atom takes over the electron belonging to the hydrogen, thus becoming a chloride ion, and the proton which is left over then shares two of the previously-unshared electrons belonging to the oxygen in a molecule of water. This is called a hydronium ion. A mixture of an indefinite but equal number of hydronium ions and chloride ions is called hydrochloric acid. It dissolves in the rest of the water.

If ammonia gas is bubbled into water, a chemical reaction also takes place between one molecule of ammonia and one molecule of water. In this case an oxygen in a water molecule takes over the electron from one of its hydrogens, forming a negatively-charged <u>hydroxyl</u> ion, OH^-, and leaving behind a proton which then shares the previously unshared electron pair on the nitrogen, forming a positively-charged <u>ammonium</u> ion, NH_4^+. A mixture of an indefinite but equal number of ammonium ions and hydroxyl ions dissolved in water forms a base, known as ammonium hydroxide.

$$NH_3 \quad + \quad H_2O \quad \rightarrow \quad NH_4^+ \quad + \quad OH^- .$$

Salts can be formed by a reaction known as neutralization, meaning neutralization of the acid properties of an acid, by adding an equivalent amount of base. Originally this fact was used to define what was meant by a base. Neutralization is a true chemical reaction, the driving force for which is the formation of a covalent compound, namely water. Thus we could write a chemical reaction equation stating that one unit of ammonium hydroxide, plus one unit of hydrochloric acid, yields one unit of ammonium chloride (it would be incorrect to call them molecules) plus two molecules of water. The ammonium and chloride ions do not take part in the reaction; they are sometimes called spectator ions:

$$H_3O^+ \quad + \quad OH^- \quad \rightarrow \quad 2\ H_2O\ .$$

Although methane, ammonia, and water all appear to have similar molecular weights (16, 17, and 18), methane is a light gas, ammonia is also a gas at room temperature, but water is a liquid. Why is water a liquid? The answer is that at room temperature many H_2O molecules are attached together with a type of bond known as the hydrogen bond. A hydrogen bond is a weak attraction, perhaps less than ten percent as strong as a covalent bond, which occurs when a hydrogen atom finds itself between two atoms having unshared electron pairs.

Because of the difference in size of the nucleus of hydrogen and oxygen, the shared electrons between oxygen and hydrogen in water are closer to the oxygen nucleus than to the hydrogen nucleus, leaving each hydrogen with a slightly positive charge. At the same time each oxygen has two unshared electron pairs, zones of negativity, and these attract the slightly-positive hydrogens. Water is a polar molecule; that is, with slightly-positive hydrogens at one side, and slightly-negative oxygen at the other, each water molecule is something like a bar magnet. It has positive and negative poles. Unshared electron pairs always try to pick up positive particles, just as a magnet lying around on a workshop bench always manages to pick up stray bits of iron.

In water, hydrogen bonds are the result of the unshared electron pairs on the oxygens attracting the positive hydrogens on adjacent water molecules. This causes liquid water H_2O units to hydrogen-bond together to form what is essentially a "wall-to-wall" molecule. If examined in only one direction the H_2O subunits would be lined up "bumper-to-bumper:"

```
H–O...H–O...H–O...H–O...H–O...H–O...H–O...H–O...H–O...H–O
  |     |     |     |     |     |     |     |     |     |
  H     H     H     H     H     H     H     H     H     H
```

Thus each hydrogen is bonded to one oxygen by a covalent bond, and also attracted to another oxygen by a much weaker hydrogen bond. This hydrogen bonding extends in all directions; we have shown only one direction. And hydrogen bonding is not limited to water; elements other than oxygen have unshared electron pairs, nitrogen being an example. Water will hydrogen-bond itself to any substance which has unshared electron pairs. Such a substance is said to be wettable. If it lacks unshared electron pairs, it is not wettable and water does not stick to it. Sugar syrup has many unshared electron pairs, from the oxygen in both the water and the sugar. A glass pitcher has unshared electron pairs on the surface of the glass. When the syrup is poured, it hydrogen-bonds to the glass surface, and drips down the outside of the pitcher. On the other hand, polyethylene lacks the unshared electron pairs on its surface, and syrup poured from a polyethylene pitcher does not drip.

Carbohydrates, a class of structural materials found chiefly in plants, contain carbon, hydrogen, and oxygen. They form many hydrogen bonds, resulting in rigidity of structure. Proteins, the principal structural material in animals, contain carbon, hydrogen, oxygen, and nitrogen. They form fewer hydrogen bonds and are less rigid. It may be only coincidence that plants lead a stationary life while animals move about from place to place. In any case, hydrogen bonds are one of the most important features of all living things.

Questions

1. Why do atoms tend to gain or lose electrons?
2. In what two ways can atoms gain or lose electrons?
3. Define covalent bond, electrovalent bond, hydrogen bond.
4. Write the structural formula for water, methane, and ammonia.

5. Explain why water is a liquid at room temperature.
6. Discuss the difference between metals and nonmetals.
7. Why does not sodium chloride have a molecular weight?
8. Define "acid" and "base" in terms of electron rearrangement.
9. Write the chemical reaction equation for neutralization.
10. What tastes sour? How many tastes are there?
11. Discuss the significance of unshared electron pairs and wettability.

Chapter 7 Reaction and Equilibrium

Ice at low temperature is completely hydrogen bonded. In an ice crystal, each H_2O molecule is hydrogen bonded to four other H_2O molecules, making a six-sided honeycomb structure. The bond angles cause the molecules to spread out into an arching network, leaving spaces or holes in the ice structure. For this reason, ice occupies more space than liquid water and ice floats on water. If it were not for this fact life would not be possible; all the oceans would have frozen solid. The expansion of water when it freezes is an important behavior with respect to soil formation by cracking rocks apart. It also breaks water pipes and automobile radiators.

When ice begins to melt, it collapses. Still largely hydrogen bonded, where a few bonds break this bridgework falls into the available holes. Thus the volume becomes smaller and smaller, reaching a point of greatest collapse near 39 degrees Fahrenheit. If it were not for this behavior, once again, life would not be possible. If water were like most liquids, when ice formed on a lake it would settle to the bottom, more ice would form and settle, and in time the whole lake would be frozen solid. In fact, the oceans of the world would freeze solid. As a result the ocean currents would cease, and human beings would find the Earth uninhabitable.

There is yet another way in which we owe our very existence to water. Liquid water contains an enormous amount of heat, and water vapor contains still more. It is the constant shifting back and forth among the three phases of water which makes the surface of the Earth tolerable to life. When a cold front moves, in its path water vapor changes to liquid water (rain), or if necessary to ice (snow). The heat which is released as a result keeps the temperature from going too low. If it could not snow we would probably freeze to death.

Likewise, when the Sun shines the snow or ice melts, and the liquid water evaporates, thus taking up the excess heat and keeping us from being burned to death by the heat from the Sun. If it were not for the layer of water vapor in our atmosphere, which absorbs heat rays (infrared), life would not be possible on Earth, at least life as we know it.

There is an equilibrium among the three phases of water. There are two kinds of equilibrium--static equilibrium and dynamic equilibrium. Static equilibrium refers to something balanced and motionless, like a teaspoon balanced on the edge of a drinking glass. We are not concerned with static equilibrium. What we are concerned with here is dynamic equilibrium. It is necessary to explain what this means.

Dynamic equilibrium is equilibrium in motion, on the run. This may be illustrated by a tale from the days when warfare consisted largely of archery. Suppose two hosts went forth to battle. One can picture them advancing across an open field. When within arrow range, they began shooting arrows at one another. Each archer could carry only a limited supply of arrows, but that did not worry him too much, because if he lived he could always shoot the enemy's arrows back at him. If the battle came to a stalemate, so that for a time the number of arrows flying through the air in one direction equalled the number of arrows flying through the air in the opposite direction, the net transfer of arrows would be zero. That is what is meant by dynamic equilibrium.

In a chemical reaction, <u>reactants</u> are being converted into <u>products</u>. By convention, when writing a chemical reaction <u>equation</u>, the reactants are noted on the left side and the products are written on the right side. Going from reactant to product is called the forward reaction, while going from product to reactant is called the reverse reaction (space metaphors). Usually a reaction can go both ways. When sufficient concentration of the products is reached, the reaction is going backward as fast as it is going forward. The reaction is then said to be in equilibrium. A chemical reaction equation provides a great deal of information in what amounts to a kind of chemical shorthand. Each time the symbol of an element appears, this means one atom of that element. Two or more symbols of elements together represent a formula, which shows the ratio in which the elements combine to form a molecule if covalent bonded, or merely a formula if electrovalent bonded. If more than one atom of an element is present, it is indicated by a subscript. Thus, a molecule of the compound, sugar, may be represented by $C_{12}H_{22}O_{11}$. This means that each molecule of sugar contains twelve atoms of carbon, twenty-two atoms of hydrogen, and eleven atoms of oxygen. The formula of salt, a non-compound, is NaCl. This merely indicates that sodium and chlorine are present in equivalent proportions; actually they are ions, as we have seen.

One thing that usually puzzles a beginning chemistry student, is how the chemist can tell by looking at a formula whether it is a covalent compound or merely a mixture of ions, or something in between. The answer is that he can not. That is not the way science is done. When the chemist looks at a formula on paper and describes the behavior of the substance, he is doing so from his memory based on experience. The experience is obtained by testing in the laboratory. For example, he knows that sugar dissolved in water does not consist of ions, because a sugar solution will not conduct an electric current; and likewise he knows that salt dissolved in water does consist of ions, because a salt solution will conduct an electric current and for this reason is called an electrolyte.

It often happens in a chemical reaction that one of the products is removed from the scene. It may be that a gas is formed, which escapes into the air; or one of the products may be insoluble and form a precipitate (it settles to the bottom of the solution); or one of the products may be immediately used up in a further reaction. In such a case the reaction equilibrium is shifted toward the right side of the equation. Let us suppose that some medieval weapon technologist had invented a very thin bowstring. The archers on his side could use arrows with narrow notches, so narrow that the enemy archers could not fit these arrows to their bowstrings and hence could not return them. The standard arrows could be returned, however; the wide notches would fit the narrow strings but not vice versa. This would upset the equilibrium described in the archery analogy above, resulting in victory for the side with the narrow bowstrings. This same principle applies to chemical and physical equilibrium.

A chemical reaction always tries to come to equilibrium. There will be some definite concentration ratio of reactants and products where this reaction equilibrium lies. Then, if excess reactant is present, the reaction will tend to go toward the right with formation of more product; and if excess product is present, the reaction will tend to go toward the left of the equation (as written) with formation of more reactant. It does this for the usual reason, of course: to get to a lower energy level. The whole process is a matter of energy. This tendency is known as le Chatelier's Principle. It would be difficult to define it more clearly than a student did when he wrote on a test paper: If to any system in equilibrium is added an upset, the system will tend to shift in such a way as to offset the upset.

There is an equilibrium among the three phases of water which may be used to illustrate physical equilibrium, since this is a physical change and not a chemical change. It is described by plotting three curved lines, which meet at a point, on what is known as the pressure-temperature diagram for water (Fig. 3). At the triple point (marked O), water can exist as a solid, a liquid, and a gas, all three phases in equilibrium at the same temperature and pressure. This means that H_2O units are interchanging just as rapidly from any one phase to any other phase. At any other temperature and pressure, the equilibrium occurs between two phases only, along the three lines. On line OA, liquid water and water vapor are in equilibrium. Thus water evaporates toward the vapor side of the line and condenses toward the liquid side of the line. On line OB, liquid water and ice are in equilibrium. It is significant that this line slants upward to the left. Because of this, ice skating is possible. The pressure of ice skate blades on the ice melts it to water for an instant, so that the skater actually glides over the surface of the ice on a thin film of liquid water.

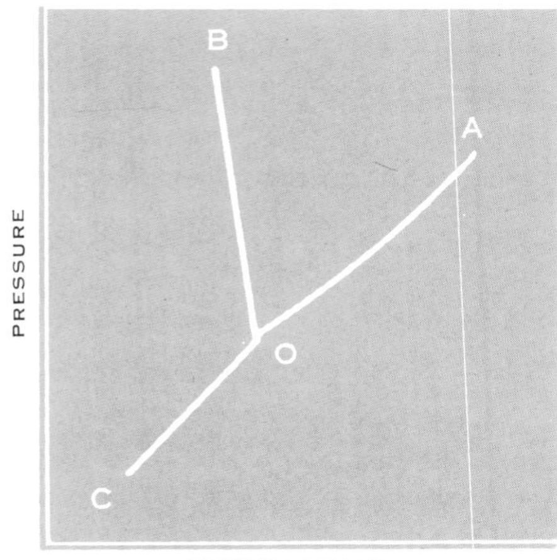

FIG. 3. PRESSURE–TEMPERATURE DIAGRAM FOR WATER.

It is also seen from line OB that when the pressure decreases, the temperature remaining constant, liquid water freezes to ice. This is the mechanism by which glaciers flow--pressure which causes melting, flow to relieve the pressure, refreezing because the pressure has been relieved but now at a new, lower location. The whole process is known as regelation. It is easily demonstrated by hanging a weighted wire over a block of ice. The wire cuts through the ice due to pressure melting it, but the ice remains a solid block because refreezing occurs as fast as the wire passes.

Line OC is known as the sublimation curve. Along this line ice and water vapor are in equilibrium. It indicates that molecular H_2O units are able to pass directly from solid ice phase to gaseous water vapor phase, without necessarily passing through an intermediate phase of liquid water. This is the way in which frozen food dries out if not properly packaged in vapor-barrier material in a freezer compartment of a refrigerator. It is also by this mechanism that laundry will dry outdoors in subzero weather. This is how most of the frost forms in freezers and refrigerators. The ice on the coils surrounding the freezing compartment is either distilled water, if condensed from some liquid left open in the refrigerator, or it is sublimed water, which is equivalent to distilled water in purity. It can be defrosted and used in car batteries. The owner of a cruiser equipped with a mechanical refrigerator does not need to come to shore to obtain distilled water for his storage batteries.

While sublimation as a physical process may not seem as familiar as evaporation or distillation, actually it is quite common. Many solid substances pass into the vapor phase in this way; in fact, all solid substances with an odor do so. It is the actual molecules resulting from sublimation which impinge on our sense of smell which tell us of the presence of camphor, moth balls, or any one of a number of solid things. Probably one of the first recorded uses of sublimation was in the preparation of eye shadow as used by the early Egyptians and other nearby civilizations. Antimony trisulfide, Sb_2S_3, was sublimed from its ore Stibnite (referred to as stibick stone in the Bible). Stibium is Latin for "mark" because it can be used as a marking pencil. It is from the Latin name that we get our symbol Sb. In the early days, however, it was referred to as Al Kohl. The Hebrews derived this word from Arabic, al meaning "the" and kohl having the connotation of "dark blue paint."

Because this eye paint was purified by sublimation, and was called Al Kohl, anything which was purified by such a method came also to be called an "al kohl." Thus, for example, sulfur was purified by sublimation, as it is to this day, and the resulting product was known as al kohl of sulfur. And finally, when it was discovered that a similar process would produce from wine a beverage much more potent than heretofore known, this was called al kohl of wine. That is how we got our present word alcohol, derived from the Arabic for the poisonous dark blue eye shadow used as a cosmetic, back when mankind on Earth was numbered in the tens of thousands and there was fear that the race might not survive. Probably there is some direct connection between the use of these products and the fact that we are here today.

An interesting hydrogen bonding situation occurs in some materials, which is known as thixotropy. Tomato catsup is an example. When a bottle of catsup is slowly inverted, it will not pour, but when shaken vigorously and then inverted suddenly, often too much pours out. This is thixotropy. It is a situation in which upon standing, so many hydrogen bonds form that the material becomes more or less rigid, but when agitated in some way sufficient of the hydrogen bonds are broken that the material will flow. Sodium bentonite is a naturally-occurring thixotropic clay which is used for many industrial purposes. There are paints on the market which do not drip from the brush or sag after being applied, and which can be washed from the brush or roller with water. They are water emulsions which exhibit thixotropy. The motion of the brush or roller breaks hydrogen bonds so that the paint flows on smoothly, but it immediately reforms hydrogen bonds and sets to a rigid system.

While water is the most common liquid on Earth, it is seldom found in pure form in nature because it is such a good solvent. It will dissolve some of practically anything, including the rocks. For many years it has been dissolving sodium chloride out of the soil and carrying it down to the sea, where the salt is left when the water evaporates. It is said that the salt dissolved in all the oceans would now be sufficient to cover all the dry land to a depth of 112 feet! We have previously seen that salt is a mixture of sodium ions and chloride ions, which are held in a crystal lattice in dry form by the attraction of opposite charges, an attraction which is known as the electrovalent bond. We have also seen that water molecules are polar, having a relatively-positive end and a relatively-negative end. It is obvious that the sodium and chloride ions would also be attracted to these charges on water.

We have previously mentioned also that a salt will dissolve if the hydration of the ions is forceful enough to pull the ions apart. Some kinds of salt, such as silver chloride ($AgCl$), are not soluble in water, while other kinds of salt, such as sodium chloride ($NaCl$) are readily soluble. This can be explained in terms of the relative energy involved. In fact, practically all changes both physical and chemical can be explained or described in terms of energy as a driving force, the tendency always being to shift in such a way as to lower the free energy of the system.

When sodium chloride crystals dissolve in water, the ions are surrounded by a number of water molecules, putting them into "water cages" which might be pictured as shown in Figure 4. This is due to attraction of opposite charges; the positive ion (Na^+) attracts the negative oxygen of several water molecules, whose unshared electrons want to sink into the sodium ion's electron "hole," and for the same reason the Cl^- ion attracts water molecules by their positive ends. There results a sort of giant ion, the size of which can be determined by its rate of migration when an electric potential is applied to the solution. What determines whether or not a salt will dissolve in water? The answer is simple. If the hydration of the ions releases an amount of energy greater than that which is required to pull the ions out of the salt crystal, then the salt dissolves because in so doing it releases energy. On the other hand, if dissolving would raise the energy of the system, the crystal does not dissolve, and the substance is said to be insoluble.

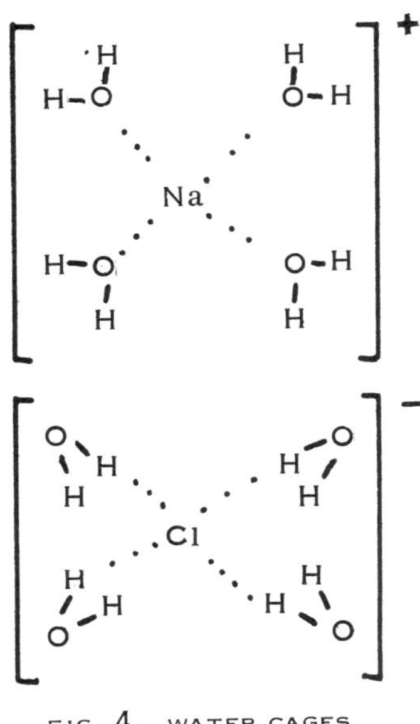

FIG. 4. WATER CAGES

Questions

1. Why does water expand when it freezes to form ice?
2. What physical properties of water make the climate of the Earth suitable for human habitation?
3. What is the difference between static and dynamic equilibrium?
4. Define chemical reaction, equation, reactant, and product.

5. Why is a salt solution called an electrolyte?
6. What is le Chatelier's principle?
7. Explain how glaciers flow, and how ice skating is possible.
8. What is sublimation? Give some common examples.
9. What is meant by thixotropy?
10. What determines whether or not a salt is soluble water?

Chapter 8 Notes About the Elements

For purposes of illustration in this book we have chosen to deal with the first eighteen elements in the Periodic Table (Table 2), with the full realization that there are many more elements (103 at the time of publication), and that this is not a complete treatment of the subject. It happens, however, that among these first elements are those most important to life, namely hydrogen, carbon, nitrogen, oxygen, sodium, magnesium, phosphorus, sulfur and chlorine. All the rest of the Periodic Table does not contain so important a list, although other elements of special significance to life are potassium, calcium, manganese, iron, cobalt, copper, zinc, iodine, and possibly a few others in very minor amounts. In order to give more meaning to these first eighteen elements, this chapter contains a brief account of each:

1. Hydrogen. This name means <u>water forming</u>, because water is formed when hydrogen burns: $2\ H_2 + O_2 \rightarrow 2H_2O$. Hydrogen is present in all of the myriads of carbon compounds of which living things consist, and much of the hydrogen on Earth is combined in the water of the oceans. Gaseous hydrogen is said to leave the Earth's atmosphere rather easily, and escape into space. Hydrogen is the simplest, lightest, and most abundant element in the Universe. According to our present knowledge of atomic structure there could never be an element lighter than hydrogen. If tomorrow's newspapers were to carry headlines: "RUSSIAN SCIENTISTS DISCOVER NEW ELEMENT LIGHTER THAN HYDROGEN," would you believe it? No doubt most readers would; by now people are ready to believe anything they read in the name of science. But if this were true it would overthrow everything we know about the structure of matter.

2. Helium. This is an inert gas, the only nonmetal with a name ending in -ium (somebody goofed). It was first discovered on the Sun by means of spectroscopy, which explains its name, which comes from Greek helios meaning Sun. Twenty-five years after it was found on the Sun it was found to occur in the Earth in certain locations, chiefly in the southwest United States. Helium is the lightest gas which will not burn or explode, hence it is the best to use for balloons. On 6 May 1937 the German dirigible Hindenburg exploded at Lakehurst, New Jersey upon arrival from a trans-Atlantic crossing. It exploded because it was filled with hydrogen; the United States would not sell helium to Germany for this purpose. This was a terrible air disaster. Deep sea divers use a helium-oxygen mixture because helium is less soluble in blood than nitrogen and does not cause "bends."

3. Lithium. This name comes from Greek lithos, meaning stone. Lithium is a light metal, not found free in nature. It is used in alloys, and in the all-purpose pressure lubricants for lubricating automobile bearings.

4. Beryllium. This name comes from a class of gems known as beryls, of which the emerald is an example. Recovery of beryllium from the ore is expensive by present processes, but these will no doubt be improved. Beryllium is a light strong metal, hard enough to scratch glass, and it has a great future in alloys for the Space Age. Our word brilliant comes from the same root.

5. Boron. This is named from borax, a naturally-occurring compound of boron, familiar in the United States from advertising by the "Twenty-Mule-Team" brand. Boron compounds have many uses, in cleansers, in water softeners, in glass, and in rocket fuel.

6. Carbon. Carbo is Latin for charcoal. Carbon is found in several forms, charcoal, lamp black, graphite, and diamond. Millions of carbon compounds are known. Chemists have made more intense study of the compounds of carbon than of any other element, no doubt because the naturally-occurring compounds of living things contain carbon. That is why they are called organic compounds,

referring to their origin in living organs. Organic chemistry is today perhaps the largest field of specialization, and it long ago ceased to refer to compounds found in nature. It includes countless compounds not found in nature, such as the synthetic fibers, plastics, etc. Charcoal has been prepared from wood and used as a smokeless fuel since earliest times; it is the coal mentioned in the Bible. Mixed with sulfur and potassium nitrate or saltpeter (KNO_3), it is black gunpowder, a discovery which changed the course of history.

7. Nitrogen. This name means nitron forming, and it results from a comedy of errors. In early literature such as the Bible, we find reference to nitron, which is Greek for soda. This was the original washing powder, found in natural deposits in the desert, and it is still sold in our stores today under the name of washing soda. The Roman Empire, in early Christian times, had street corner urine collectors, whom we know about because they were taxed by the government. They collected urine, allowed it to putrify, and sold it for a household cleanser. Not knowing what we now know about chemistry, it appeared that this urine came to contain nitron or soda; at least it cleaned like nitron. When later it was found to contain an element, this element was named nitrogen, meaning "giving rise to nitron!" The urine did not contain soda, however; its cleansing action was due to the formation of ammonia, which combined with carbon dioxide from the air, yielding ammonium carbonate, which is a good cleanser. The ammonia came from decomposition of urea, a nitrogen compound in urine. Free nitrogen gas, N_2, constitutes about 78 percent of our atmosphere. Nitrogen is very necessary to life; it is the distinctive element in the compounds called proteins, which are the physical basis of protoplasm, the living substance in life as it is known on this planet.

8. Oxygen. This name means acid forming. It is no longer a good name. Free oxygen gas, O_2, constitutes about 21 percent of the air we breathe, without which we could not live. It is necessary for the reactions of respiration in most living cells, and it is likewise necessary

for the combustion of fuels in devices ranging from furnaces through railway locomotives, automobiles, airplanes, to rockets and space missiles. Oxygen is the most abundant element on Earth, much of it being combined with other elements in the rocks and in water. Oxygen is definitely one of the "best things of life (which) are free!"

9. Fluorine. This name comes from Latin fluo, meaning to flow. Fluorine is a poison gas which eats glass, but fluoride ions are used in fluoridation of drinking water supplies.

10. Neon. This name means new. Neon is an inert gas, and it is familiar from the red glow of countless neon advertising signs seen in cities at night.

11. Sodium. This element gets its name from the same source as nitrogen! The Greek nitron, in Latin becomes natrium, which is the source of the symbol Na for sodium. Nitron in Italian (and in English) is soda, a word which really means headache; apparently soda was used as a treatment for headache. The chemical name of soda is sodium carbonate, Na_2CO_3. There is also baking soda which has the formula $NaHCO_3$. Both are familiar household items. Sodium is a soft metal which is not found free in nature. When placed on water it decomposes the water violently with liberation of hydrogen and usually the hydrogen bursts into flame from the heat generated. Sodium is a common constituent of many salts and compounds, the most familiar being ordinary table salt, NaCl. The desert people of ancient times got salt-chalk deposits from the dry desert. They crushed the lumps in a cloth bag, swished in boiling water to get rid of the bitter magnesium ions (magnesium chloride, $MgCl_2$), then soaked the NaCl out of the chalk with cold water, and evaporated off the water to get salt crystals. This was clever chemical engineering, because magnesium chloride is very soluble in hot water but not sodium chloride. Salt has always played an important part in history and in the migrations of mankind; in the East it is a symbol of hospitality: "There is salt between us." The small boy said "Salt is what makes oatmeal taste bad when you forget to put any in."

12. Magnesium. This is named after Magnesia, a district in Greece. Magnesium is a light metal, inexpensive, which is widely used in alloys, in signal flares, and in many important compounds. It is used medicinally in the form of "milk of magnesia," which is magnesium hydroxide ($Mg(OH)_2$), and "epsom salts," which is magnesium sulfate ($MgSO_4$). Magnesium ions in water have a bitter taste, as we mentioned when discussing sodium. The Japanese long ago found that the salt they obtained by evaporating sea water could be debittered by heating it in a pan, whereupon a white cloud would rise up. This was magnesium chloride. It could be collected, and used for precipitating soy bean curds, which because of this discovery became an important part of the Japanese diet and an early example of cheese making. Magnesium ions, or possibly also calcium ions, were very likely the cause of the bitterness of the "bitter water of Marah" which Moses encountered in the wilderness. Persons familiar with this country today say that such bitter pools are common. The location of this one is uncertain because Marah is not a place, it merely means "bitter." It happens that the method by which Moses debittered this water makes good scientific sense. It is known that wood oxidises in the desert from long exposure to the ultraviolet rays of the desert sun and exposure to the oxygen in the air, forming oxidised cellulose which is capable of removing calcium and magnesium ions from water by a process known as ion exchange. A similar process is widely used today for softening water.

13. Aluminum. This name comes from its ancient source, alum, or potassium aluminum sulfate, long used as a mordant in dyeing cotton textiles (see the chapter on the colloidal state of matter). It is called aluminium in most countries, in accord with the practice of using an -<u>ium</u> ending for metals, but attempts to make this name stick in the United States have failed. Aluminum a hundred years ago was a very rare metal, worth as much as ninety dollars a pound. Today it is one of our cheapest and most abundant metals. When the Washington Monument was built, Congress appropriated the money to have the top capped with this very unusual metal, aluminum!

14. Silicon. This element gets its name from the Latin silex, meaning flint. It is not found free in nature, but combined with oxygen is sand (silica, SiO_2) , quartz, agate, flint, jasper, and a part of many other rocks. It makes up about twenty-five percent of the Earth's crust. Silicon is a nonmetal much like carbon in many ways; in fact carbon-type compounds are made using silicon instead of carbon. These are called silicones. Among them are lubricants which can stand very high temperatures. The famous artist Whistler (Whistler's Mother) apparently failed at West Point because of silicon. At least he is said to have stated that if silicon had been a gas he would have become a brigadier general.

15. Phosphorus. The name means light bearing. Phosphorus glows in the dark, especially if rubbed. The free element is not found in nature. It is necessary to life, and is found in many very important biochemical compounds, including the genes which transmit our heredity. It is said as a result of research with radioactive phosphorus that once a phosphorus atom enters into a DNA molecule, as the gene is called, it never comes out. Since these molecules are transmitted from generation to generation, there is then the possibility that you or I might have at least one atom of phosphorus in our genes which came directly from Cleopatra, or Napoleon, or whomever one might choose providing the person had children.

16. Sulfur. Pure sulfur was known to early man from its occurrence at the brink of volcanoes (brimstone), and in natural deposits which sometimes caught fire and suggested an image of hell. The name has always been sulfur; its origin is unknown. Usage also has it spelled sulphur, but this came later. Sulfur is necessary to life. Sulfuric acid, H_2SO_4, is the acid found in auto batteries and is also the basis of the heavy chemical industry.

17. Chlorine. This is a greenish-yellow gas, named from the Greek chloros, which describes its color. It is irritating to the respiratory tract. The Germans introduced it into warfare as a "poison gas" in 1915. Actually it is not deadly in the modern sense. It is one of

the most important and necessary of elements. Chlorine gas is used for water treatment, without which modern cities could not survive. Its ion is part of sodium chloride, NaCl.

18. Argon. This is a Greek word meaning inactive. Air contains nearly one percent argon. It is extracted from the air and used to fill electric light bulbs and fluorescent light tubes, where it does not react with the hot filaments because it is an inert gas. Information about other elements will be found in physical science textbooks listed under Suggested Reading.

Questions

1. How did hydrogen get its name?
2. What type of element would be expected if its name ends with -ium?
3. Why is helium used in deep sea diving?
4. Why are compounds of carbon called organic compounds?
5. How did nitrogen get its name?
6. Why is oxygen necessary for human life?
7. What does the element phosphorus have to do with heredity?
8. What is the relation between Whistler's Mother (picture) and silicon?
9. How does chlorine gas make modern cities possible?

Chapter 9 The Colloidal State

Emerson, the American philosopher wrote, "We live amidst surfaces, and the true art of life is to skate well on them." This is quite literally true. It has been found that all living systems, and the majority of non-living systems as well, exist in a state known as the colloidal state. This is a type of dispersion, somewhere between a true solution and a suspension, in which the ratio of surface area to total mass is so great that the surface properties become the dominating properties of the system.

The word colloidal literally means glue-like, and it is not a good word to use because it is not at all necessary for a colloidal system to be glue-like. And the word surface is not so good either, because it applies only to the place at which a solid or liquid phase is exposed to a gas phase such as the air. A surface is a special case of an interface, hence we shall henceforth speak of interfaces. An interface is where two phases meet. We have already mentioned that matter can exist in three different phases: solid, liquid, and gas. If a system has only one phase, it is said to be homogeneous. Small molecules such as sugar molecules, and small ions such as those in sodium chloride, form solutions which have only one phase and are therefore homogeneous. But if we consider the container holding either of these solutions as a part of the system, then the system has two phases namely the solution and the walls of the container. Where the two phases meet we find a solution-container interface.

If sand is suspended in water, it forms a suspension which has two phases, sand and water. And it has sand-water interfaces. This is an example of a heterogeneous system. If the sand is ground very fine, so fine that the grains of sand are invisible even in the best optical microscope, they will not settle out upon standing, and then we have a colloidal system. Such a system is still heterogeneous, and it is called a sol. The word sol is not an abbreviation for solution.

Water flowing from a glacier contains such colloidal-size sand particles. This water as a result has a greenish appearance. It is called glacial milk. If we allow the boulders, rocks, sand, and silt to settle out, the colloidal particles still remain suspended. They are called micelles. Examined with an ordinary microscope, such a sol looks perfectly clear. However, if a bright beam of light is directed across a sol in the dark, examination with a high-powered microscope reveals bright pin-points of light dancing and jiggling around in a zig-zag fashion. These little sparks of light reveal where the colloidal micelles are, and it shows why they do not settle out. They are in constant rapid aimless motion.

This experiment shows that the water molecules, which cannot be seen at all, and the colloidal micelles, which emit the flashes of light, are both in constant rapid motion. When a micelle collides unevenly with water molecules, it rebounds from this collision and this is the cause of its movement. The movement is called Brownian motion. If it were not for the frequent collisions with the constantly-moving water molecules, the micelles would settle to the bottom of the container.

If a narrow beam of light is projected through a colloidal sol in a completely dark room, the path of light scatters and fans out as it strikes the colloidal micelles. True solutions do not produce this effect. The cone-shaped beam of light is known as a Tyndall cone. It can frequently be observed in nature. When a sunbeam breaks forth through an opening in an overcast sky, it strikes the dust in the air and widens as it comes down to the Earth. In a large railroad station in a city, a beam of sunlight from a small window high up a wall produces a pronounced Tyndall cone as it passes through the dusty air to the floor.

The behavior of matter in the colloidal state is unusual, due to the high amount of interfacial area and the great quantity of energy contained in the interface. The colloidal state is an activated state; it is more reactive than matter in mass, that is, in large chunks. Part of this energy is expended in the separation of electrical charges. Every colloidal micelle is electrically charged. Some kinds of colloidal micelle are always positive, some kinds are always negative, and some can change from positive to negative depending upon conditions. But a colloidal micelle is never without a charge. Without a charge it would not remain in suspension. It is the repulsion of a like charge on each of the micelles which holds the micelles apart, preventing them from coalescing together to form aggregates large enough to settle out.

If a small amount of salt is added to a colloidal sol, the protective effect of the charges on the micelles is quenched, and the colloidal sol precipitates or settles out. The mechanism involved is too technical to go into here. This phenomenon, the precipitation of a sol by addition of an electrolyte, is a factor in the formation of river deltas. As a river flows down to the sea, it carries particles of soil and rock with it. As the flow rate of the river slows down, the silt settles out but the sols remain in suspension andare carried out to sea. There they are precipitated by the salt in the ocean. As a result, there are major cities which at one time in past history were major seaports which now lie far inland because the delta has built the land out beyond them.

Human blood plasma contains protein (a nitrogen compound) which is colloidal. The interfacial area of these blood plasma micelles in an adult human amounts to approximately forty acres. This enormous area serves to pick up food molecules by adsorption and transport them wherever the blood flows to the various organs and tissues, over a pipeline of blood capillaries which in the muscle system alone is equal to two and one-half times the distance around the earth. On their return trip these micelles which have left nutrients behind where they are needed pick up waste molecules from the cells and bring them back to be dumped. Blood banks preserve this colloidal blood plasma to administer intravenously to persons who need it in an emergency, such as may result from loss of blood. Another important function of this blood plasma colloid is to help hold the water in the blood stream, maintaining the necessary blood pressure. There are synthetic colloids which are used for this purpose in addition to blood plasma, as blood "extenders."

An American scientist named Cottrell (1877-1948) invented a device called the Cottrell precipitator which removes charged smoke particles from a smoke stack. The device consists essentially of a set of metal plates which are kept charged with electricity, some of the plates having a positive charge and the other plates a negative charge. The smoke particles are attracted to the plate with the opposite charge, where they accumulate and drop to the bottom of the stack to be scraped out.

The first Cottrell precipitator was used at a lead smelter in California in 1908. One of the largest and most famous of these installations was placed in the "largest stack in the world," at Anaconda, Montana, in 1919. As a result the company recovered arsenic compounds from the smoke and became a leading producer of arsenic. Not all particles of smoke are in the colloidal size range, but many of them are. The blue side-stream rising from a lighted cigarette is largely colloidal. Cottrell turned over the money received for use of the process to a non-profit Research Corporation, to be used in helping other scientists who need money to do research, and this has today grown into a major source of research grants.

Most of the everyday materials we encounter are in the colloidal state. When we get up in the morning we may wash with colloidal soap or a colloidal detergent, dress in colloidal clothing dyed with colloidal dyes, eat a colloidal breakfast while perhaps reading a colloidal newspaper printed with colloidal ink. Then we may walk to school or work on a colloidal concrete sidewalk, or drive to work or school on colloidal pavement in an automobile made with colloidal alloys, on colloidal tires. In the classroom or office we may take notes with a colloidal pencil or a pen filled with colloidal ink, writing on colloidal paper. We eat a colloidal lunch. Coffee, tea, wine, and beer are colloidal sols. Milk is an emulsion stabilized by a colloidal sol. It would be possible to go on and on; in fact, it is difficult to list more than a few common household articles which are not colloidal. Our bodies are entirely colloidal, as is all living substance.

Dyes are colloidal, and the principle of attraction of opposite charges is used in dyeing cloth. If one can obtain from a chemistry or microbiology laboratory, dilute sols of methylene blue (blue color), and acid fuchsin (red color), and some strips of filter paper, the difference of charge and its effect can be demonstrated in a few minutes. This is possible because filter paper (cellulose, cotton cloth, etc.) in contact with water has a negative charge at its interface. The water in turn has a positive charge when in contact with cellulose. In water, methylene blue has a positive charge and acid fuchsin has a negative charge.

If a strip of filter paper is suspended so that the bottom end dips into the methylene blue sol, the blue dye does not rise above the surface of the liquid. This is because methylene blue micelles are strongly attracted to the oppositely-charged paper. They dye the paper, precipitating out on it, creating a dense blue zone just at the surface of the liquid. On the other hand the acid fuchsin, having a negative charge the same as the paper, is not attracted to the paper at all and is swept along with the water as it rapidly rises due to capillary attraction. The red sol reaches the top of the filter paper strip in a few minutes. The clear colorless water from the blue sol also rises just as rapidly to the top of its strip.

In order to dye cotton cloth, which is negatively charged in contact with water, one must use a positively-charged dye. Once this dye has penetrated into the fibers, it may be precipitated there by adding salt to the water. This makes the dye particles too large to wash away when the cloth is laundered. If the dye happens to be negatively-charged, it is still possible to use it to dye cotton, by use of the mordant process. Usually the mordant is a salt of aluminum, alum being used for this purpose by the ancients long before the element aluminum had been discovered. A glance at the Periodic Table will show that aluminum is in Group 3, hence the aluminum ion is Al^{+3}. It can precipitate on the negative cotton fibers and have positive charge left over to attract a negative dye.

The dyeing of wool and silk is a different problem, because these are proteins. Proteins are large complex molecules, so large that they are colloidal micelles, and they can be made either negative or positive by adding base or acid to the water in which they are immersed. Thus wool fibers or silk fibers can be dyed with a dye of either charge by adjusting the charge on the fiber to be opposite. The American Indians in the southwestern United States were well aware of this process, and they used ashes from their wood fires (potash) to make the dye bath alkaline, so that their positively-charged dyes would stick to the wool.

The surface of a liquid has special properties. It behaves much like a tightly-stretched skin. This tension at the surface of a liquid such as water can be explained by the unbalanced forces of molecular attraction at the surface, as shown in Figure 5. This stretching effect is known as surface tension. Molecules of water, individual H_2O units down in the body of the liquid, are surrounded by other H_2O molecules on all sides to which they are attracted by hydrogen bonding equally in all directions. The forces thus counter balance each other, so that an individual H_2O unit is more or less free to move.

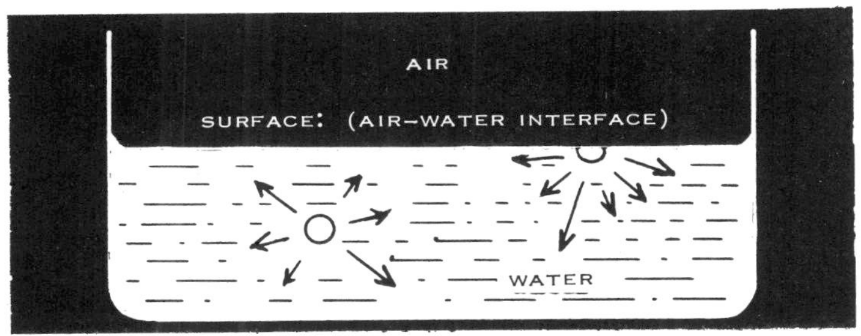

FIG. 5. DIAGRAM ILLUSTRATING THE UNBALANCED FORCES OF ATTRACTION FOR MOLECULE IN THE SURFACE.

In the surface the H_2O units are pulled downward and to each side, but not upward. The result is this tightly stretched "skin" of water molecules on the surface. If one very carefully lays a needle on this surface, it will float. If a glass full of water is very slowly filled still more, the water will heap up slightly above the top of the brim. It is this arching effect which causes water to rise in a very narrow tube, or on cloth or filter paper, the force called capillary attraction.

Large creatures such as humans have an omnipresent fear of falling and being injured. For little creatures, this fear of falling (which would do no harm) is replaced by fear of being pushed under the surface film of water. An insect could be dropped from a high building or an airplane and land without being harmed, but to an insect the surface of a water pond is as formidable as boards nailed over the surface preventing escape. Many insects show elaborate adaptations to avoid being trapped under such a surface. There are butterflies which have developed a long proboscis, and insects with unwettable feet which walk on water surfaces. Mosquito larvae cling to this "skin".

Surface tension is only a special case of the general case of interfacial tension. Wherever two phases meet, there is interfacial tension, and this is where part of the great energy content of a colloidal system is stored. Any substance which can crowd into an interface and lower this tension will decrease the energy content, and hence will tend to do so. This is because all systems always try to reach the lowest energy state possible, as we have frequently mentioned before. This is the incentive for all chemical and physical changes. Concentration at an interface of anything which lowers interfacial tension is called adsorption. Very often colloids are involved in adsorption processes because they have so great an interfacial area per unit mass.

A catalyst is a substance which lowers the energy of activation of a reaction, thus hastening its attainment of equilibrium. It is not used up in the reaction. Activation energy is discussed in the chapter on energy. Certain types of catalysts operate by adsorption. Spongy platinum black is platinum metal, spread out thin on a very great surface area so that it has colloidal properties. If oxygen gas and hydrogen gas are mixed and passed over such a surface, they are adsorbed with such great pressure that they pull apart into individual hydrogen and oxygen atoms, as shown in Figure 6. These atoms being very reactive, react with each other immediately to form molecules of water, and the energy thereby released is so great that the platinum black is heated red hot. Devices of this sort have been made into cigarette lighters, caps for auto batteries which save the hydrogen that is released during charging and return it as water, and pocket hand warmers.

HOHHOHHOHHOHHOH

FIG. 6. DIAGRAM ILLUSTRATING HYDROGEN AND OXYGEN ATOMS ON PLATINUM BLACK CATALYST.

A demonstration of adsorption catalysis can be made by wrapping some bare copper wire (about No. 24) around a pencil making a coil about one inch long, with ends long enough to hook over a rod so that the copper coil can be suspended in a laboratory glass beaker as shown in Figure 7. Acetone (available from a drug store) is poured into the beaker so that its surface is about half an inch below the copper coil. The copper coil is removed, heated to redness in a gas flame, and immediately returned to its position in the beaker. The copper coil will continue to glow red hot indefinitely.

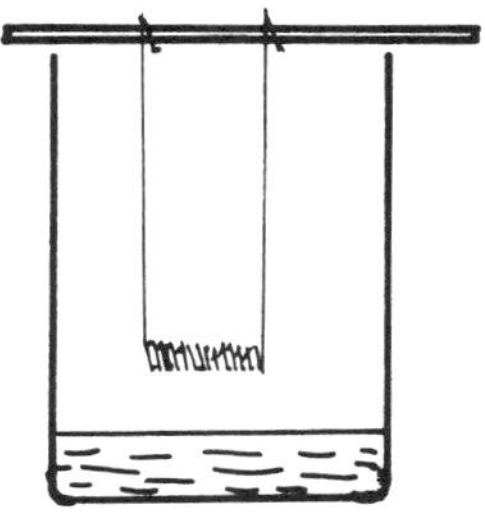

FIG. 7. APPARATUS FOR CATALYSIS.

Probably this is how it happens: (a) Heating the copper wire causes it to combine with oxygen from the air, forming a coating of copper oxide, CuO. (b) When acetone vapor reaches the hot copper wire, the oxygen is pulled away from the copper to combine with hydrogen in the acetone, forming water and thus giving off heat. (c) This heat reheats the wire, so that it again combines with oxygen from the air, and the process is repeated. This can be continued for several hours if desired. This demonstration should be done with caution, because acetone is flammable.

When a substance is adsorbed, this lowers interfacial energy and energy is released. Usually this released energy is converted into heat, known as the heat of adsorption. This is what happens in whipped egg white, or meringue. Air is whipped into the egg white forming a gas-solid colloidal system known as a <u>foam</u>. The heat given off by adsorption of the egg white on the great surface area produced cooks the egg protein, so that it becomes rigid. A whipped egg white is cooked; it is not raw.

In industrial processes, specially-prepared carbon with an immense surface area is often used to adsorb undesired colors from liquids, such as wine for example. The coloring matter clings to this activated charcoal or decolorizing carbon because it adsorbs, lowering interfacial tension. One can easily demonstrate this by mixing a tablespoon of decolorizing carbon with a cola drink, shaking thoroughly and allowing it to stand for ten or fifteen minutes at room temperature. Upon pouring the cola through a folded filter paper on a funnel, it will be seen that the liquid which passes through has lost its color and will be colorless like water. Its taste will usually be unchanged.

Since adsorption is defined as the concentration at an interface of any substance which lowers interfacial tension, it might be expected that a substance which would raise interfacial tension will actually shun an interface. Such is actually found to be the case; material of this sort will stay away from a surface or interface and crowd into the interior of the liquid. An interesting example of this is the experimental finding that the surface of the ocean contains a very thin layer which does not have salt.

An emulsion consists of globules of one liquid dispersed in another. The globules themselves are usually much larger than colloidal size, but they are a colloidal system because they are stabilized by colloidal emulsifying agents. An emulsifier is any colloidal substance which concentrates at an oil-water type of interface, thus lowering interfacial tension. In general, there are two types of emulsifiers: (a) Those having many unshared electron pairs. These form emulsions of the oil-in-water type. Milk is such an emulsion. (b) Those having few if any unshared electron pairs. These form emulsions of the water-in-oil type, of which cosmetic "vanishing" cream is an example.

The first type (a) is of course water wettable. Examples are finely powdered glass or sand, and the lactoglobulin in milk which emulsifies the butter fat globules in milk. Such emulsifiers are called hydrophilic, an adjective which means "water-loving." The second type (b) is not water wettable; instead it is oil wettable and is said to be oleophilic, meaning "oil-loving." An example of an oleophilic emulsifier is finely powdered carbon black, such as is used in oil paints.

It is possible to understand how these emulsifiers act. If a mixture of oil and water, such as vinegar and olive oil as used in salad dressing, is shaken together without an emulsifying agent, upon allowing to stand it will quickly separate, the oil rising to the top layer and the water forming the layer below. However, with an emulsifier present, such as egg white, an emulsion will be formed upon shaking, and the oil and water will not separate upon standing. Whether it is an oil-in-water or a water-in-oil type of emulsion depends upon the type of emulsifier used. This is determined by the wettability of the emulsifier. If it is oil wettable it will cling to the oil side of the interface, and if it is water wettable it will cling to the water side. Upon shaking the oil water mixture with the emulsifier present, both oil globules and water globules will form according to chance, but only one type will be permanent (Fig. 8).

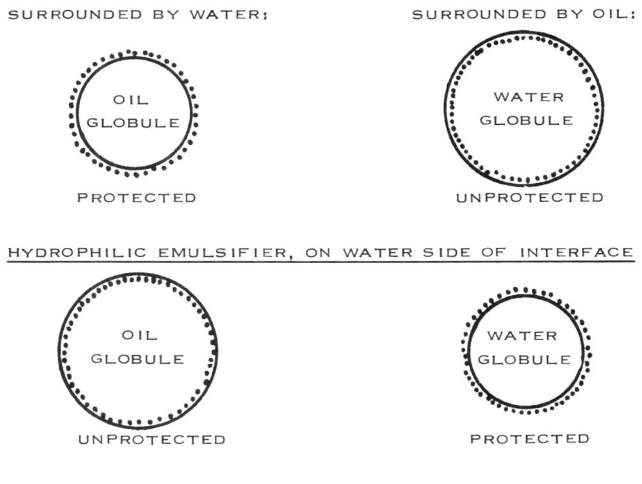

FIG. 8. DIAGRAMS ILLUSTRATING EMULSIFIER THEORY.

Only a small amount of emulsifier is required to emulsify a large amount of liquid. The fat in one's food must first be emulsified before it is digested. The emulsifier used for this purpose is known as bile. Mayonnaise and other salad dressings, liquid floor wax and automobile wax, and the types of paints which can be cleaned from the brush with water, are common examples of emulsions. Milk is probably the most familiar emulsion.

Ore flotation is a process of separating small amounts of oil wettable ore from very large amounts of water wettable rocks. The material is progressively reduced in size until it is a fine powder, then it is mixed with water and a flotation oil. By bubbling air through the mixture the oil and ore form a foam, which can be skimmed off the surface of the water. The rock powder being wettable, sinks to the bottom of the water and is washed away and discarded. Such a flotation process is used to separate copper sulfide ore at Anaconda, Montana; and to separate molybdenum sulfide ore at Climax, Colorado. A similar method has been developed to separate seed peas from weed seeds.

A similar principle is used in getting rid of oil slicks on the surface of harbors. It sometimes occurs that a large quantity of oil is spilled at a waterfront, and this oil floating on the water is a fire hazard as well as a dirty nuisance. Ordinary sand is water wettable, due to the many unshared electron pairs on the oxygen (SiO_2), but these unshared electron pairs can be covered over by roasting the sand with tar. The tar forms a thin oil wettable layer on the grains of sand. When the sand is sprayed out over an oil slick, it clings to the oil and "drowns" the oil slick, the weight of the sand causing the oil to sink to the bottom of the bay.

So far, we have seen that liquid colloidal suspensions are called sols, and that there are two types, those with water wettable micelles which are known as hydrophilic sols, and those with oil wettable micelles which are known as oleophilic sols. Sometimes the latter are called hydrophobic, which means "water fearing." There is also a type of colloidal system which is not liquid and will not flow. This type is called a gel. If the colloidal micelles are hydrophilic, and are able to trap sufficient water so that there is no liquid water left in the system, it becomes rigid. The word gel means the same thing as our more familiar word jelly. Ordinary fruit jelly is an example of a gel. Jell-o brand gelatin dessert is also an example of a gel. It consists of long threadlike gelatin molecules, which are water wettable and due to their shape have an unusually large interfacial area. Hence they can immobilize a great deal of water, and it is possible to make a rigid gel containing only two percent gelatin. The water which surrounds each thread is attracted to it largely by hydrogen bonding. The whole system becomes a sort of wall-to-wall-molecule.

One delicious example of a gel is a lemon pie. In this case it is a starch gel that is involved. Everyone has observed that upon standing, droplets of sweet liquid appear on the surface of a lemon pie. These droplets are formed by water leaking out of the gel. As time passes, the starch molecules which form the gel begin to find ways in which they can hydrogen bond directly to each other. This squeezes out the water. This water rises to the surface, carrying with it everything it can dissolve, including sugar, flavor, color, etc. This phenomenon is called syneresis.

When a person receives a skin cut, it begins to bleed, and normally a blood clot forms which soon stops the bleeding. This blood clot is a gel. After this clot is formed, it must undergo syneresis, a process known as clot retraction. If this syneresis does not occur, blood oozes out through the gel, and this is a serious condition.

The fruit jelly which housewives sometimes make, or buy at a store, is a gel formed from a hydrophilic substance known as pectin. In order to make a pectin jelly with the desired properties, the amount of sugar and the acidity must be just right. This is easily controlled in food laboratories. Much of the guess work has been taken out of home preparation of jellies by use of mixtures of dry pectin, sugar, and citric acid now on the market. From a scientific standpoint, the sugar in fruit jelly is not there for the purpose of making it sweet. It is there for the purpose of competing for water. Sugar contains many oxygens and is a terrific hydrogen bonder. The cooking of a fruit jelly is for the purpose of removing excess water. Jelly can be made without cooking. And the color and flavor have nothing to do with the gel formation.

The capacity of a hydrophilic colloidal system to hold water is called its imbibition capacity. It is this which is largely responsible for the swelling and turgidity of living cells. It is the bloom of youth. As cells grow older, they change just like the lemon pie: they find new ways to cross link and undergo syneresis. The once-firm body tissues no longer hold sufficient water to keep their firmness. They become soft and flabby, and the skin wrinkles. This marks the onset of senility. The arteries, too, find new ways to cross link, thus squeezing out the water which serves as their plasticizer and becoming tough, dry gels. This is familiarly known as "hardening of the arteries."

Imbibition capacity depends, among other factors, upon the acidity of the system. It is rather interesting that an animal, which loses its imbibition capacity and becomes progressively more soft and flabby in old age, accumulates lactic acid after death which reverses the process. The whole body once again becomes turgid and firm. This condition, so much like youth, is known as rigor mortis.

The whole field of detergents involves colloidal phenomena. We shall take soap as an example. Soap is a colloidal polar compound. We have already seen that water is a polar compound, due to its separation of partial positive and negative charges. There is another kind of polarity, in which one end of the molecule is water wettable and the other end is oil wettable. With a suitable molecule, this leads to molecular orientation.

This can be illustrated by the example of logs floating on a lake. The logs will be lying flat on the surface of the lake. However, if a heavy rock is tied to each log, it will sink to the bottom of the lake and stay there. On the other hand, if the relation of the weight of the rock to the buoyancy of the log is just right, the rock will sink and hold the log partially submerged, with one end sticking out of the water. This is how soap molecules line up at an oil-water interface (Fig. 9). Usually, a soiled place on clothing which does not wash clean readily with plain water, contains greasy dirt. The soap molecules penetrate to this oil interface and cling there, adsorbing because they lower the interfacial tension. They are lined up with the hydrophilic end in the water side and the oleophilic end in the oily side of the interface. This loosens the dirt and allows it to be carried away by agitation. Similar principles apply to the many modern detergents used in place of soap.

Ordinary soap is a sodium or potassium salt of a fatty acid, a long chain of carbons and hydrogens hooked together like the tail on a kite. This type of soap is hydrophilic. However, if the sodium or potassium ions are replaced by calcium or magnesium ions, the soap becomes hydrophobic and insoluble in water. This is what happens when soap is used in hard water, which is water containing calcium or magnesium ions, or both.

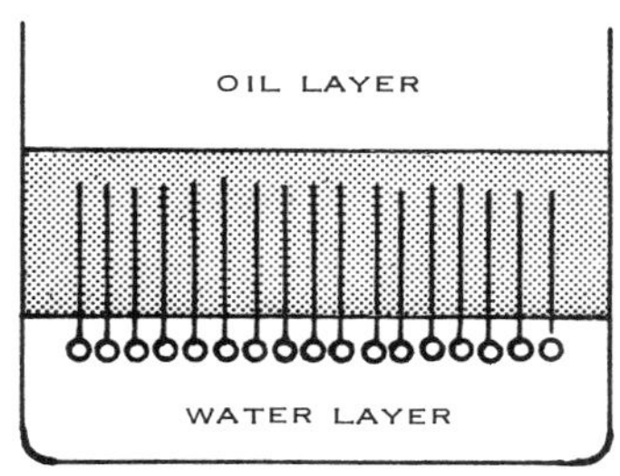

FIG. 9. DIAGRAM ILLUSTRATING ORIENTATION OF SOAP MOLECULES AT AN OIL-WATER INTERFACE.

The insoluble soap precipitates on clothing, making it appear dingy, and on hair, making it appear dull; the "ring" around a bathtub is formed by this insoluble soap. But calcium and magnesium soaps have a use--they make good hard bearing grease or "axle grease" as it was known in the horse and buggy days. Nowadays lithium soap is used, because it has been found to be superior.

In summary, the colloidal state of matter is a realm in which matter and energy meet with striking results. Because colloidal systems consist of dispersed matter having its usual chemical reactivity but now greatly magnified, and at the same time consist of interfacial areas so very great that the energy contained at these interfaces is the dominant feature, this is a condition in which matter is under great tension and stress. It is the active state of matter. This is all the more interesting because it is also the state in which living matter occurs. If one becomes familiar with elementary principles of colloids, some of which are outlined in this chapter, and keeps his eyes open, he will find countless new examples of colloidal behavior. This is an enriching experience, because it helps us appreciate the kind of world God has created, and put us in. To know about this world, as a way of learning about God through His handiwork, is the first purpose of science.

Questions

1. Define phase, interface, homogeneous, heterogeneous, sol.
2. Explain Brownian motion, and the Tyndall effect.
3. Why is the behavior of matter in the colloidal state unusual?
4. How is delta formation related to the salt in the seas?
5. What did Cottrell do with the wealth resulting from his invention?
6. Name half a dozen or so common items which are <u>not</u> in the colloidal state.
7. Explain how a mordant is used in dyeing cotton cloth.
8. What charge does cotton, or cellulose, have when immersed in water?
9. Why does the surface of a liquid behave like a stretched skin?
10. What do we call concentration at an interface of a substance because it lowers interfacial tension?
11. Give an example of a catalyst, and explain its relation to adsorption.
12. Why is whipped egg white no longer uncooked egg?
13. Which type of emulsion will be formed by use of a hydrophilic emulsifier?
14. What is a rigid hydrophilic colloidal system called?
15. Define syneresis, imbibition capacity, and molecular orientation.

Chapter 10 The Concept of Energy

We come now to the last of the four concepts: the concept of energy. The word comes from the Greek "energos," meaning "active." Energy has various meanings in everyday life, and for this reason is no more satisfactory as a word-symbol of science standing for our concept of the ultimate physical aspect of reality, than are the word-symbols which we have previously discussed, space, time, and matter.

Apparently everything is energy in some form or other. It is the stuff of the universe. It is what was created in space and time. To define it in an absolute sense would be to pile metaphor on metaphor. Hence the scientist merely defines it by what it <u>does</u>: energy is the capacity to do work.

Early man must have conceived of energy first of all from witnessing the mighty forces of nature--lightning, tornado, volcano, and hurricane. By contrast his own energy was puny; it came by the sweat of his brow. Later he used beasts of burden, waterwheels, and sailboats. He controlled fire to keep warm, frighten away animals, and cook food. Boiled food made possible the first toothless old age, with which came pain and suffering, followed by wisdom. But control of fire was not his first source of chemical energy. The first energy used directly by man, and his chief source for at least ninety-eight percent of his existence, has been the energy released in his own body by the biochemical reactions of digestion and metabolism. It was this energy which kept his body warm, drove his vital processes, and allowed his muscles to move.

Plants store energy from the sun, through the processes of photosynthesis. The storage of energy from the sun, and its subsequent release by living things, is essentially a shuffling back-and-forth of electrons between carbon orbitals and oxygen orbitals.

Removing the hydrogen from water is the first step in obtaining energy from the sun. When this happens, it is really a matter of electrons being torn from oxygen orbitals. Hydrogen with its small nucleus is a rich source of electrons; many rocket fuels are merely concentrated sources of hydrogen. When the two electrons are torn from their oxygen-hydrogen orbitals in water, this puts energy into the system much like winding up a clock spring. Of course the two tiny hydrogen nuclei (protons) go along where the electrons go.

Usually the hydrogens are attached to carbon atoms, making the many carbon compounds such as fats, carbohydrates, and proteins which make up living organs and the food we eat. It is for this reason that the chemistry of carbon compounds is called <u>organic</u> chemistry, although modern organic chemistry includes millions of compounds which are not known to occur in nature. The simplest example of an organic compound, chosen not because it is a foodstuff but because it will illustrate the point, is methane, CH_4.

Let us suppose that the four hydrogens have been put on carbon to make a molecule of methane. This winds up the "spring" because there is more energy when these hydrogens are covalent bonded to carbon than when they are covalent bonded to oxygen. How can we get this energy out of methane?

One answer is that we can get the energy out of methane by burning it. Methane is "natural gas." When the electrons go flying back to oxygen so much energy is released that a flame is produced, or even an explosion. The chemical reaction is as follows:

$$CH_4 + 2\ O_2 \rightarrow CO_2 + 2\ H_2O \qquad \text{(energy is released)}$$

In words, this chemical reaction equation reads: One molecule of methane reacts with two molecules of oxygen (under the proper conditions) to yield one molecule of carbon dioxide, two molecules of water, and energy (heat). The formation of carbon dioxide releases energy too, but little in comparison to the amount released by the formation of water.

First some energy must be put in to get the reaction started. One way of putting this energy into the system would be with a lighted match. Every chemical reaction which is able to happen, and has not already happened, must first be activated in some way. The energy required to get it going is called activation energy. The gasoline in the tank of an automobile can unite with the oxygen from the air to which it is exposed, but it does not do so until the activation energy is supplied by the spark plugs firing in the engine. Likewise the sugar in a sugar bowl can unite with the oxygen of the air to give off energy, but this does not happen until the sugar is either heated until it burns, or until it is eaten and the enzymes in a living system catalyze the chemical reaction without flame or explosion.

Every living system, including human beings, owes his continued life to the presence of "energy humps" which stand in the way of reactions until they are activated. If it were not for this all of our chemical reactions would go at once with disastrous results. These energy humps can be likened to a log, placed in front of a car parked at the edge of a cliff. The car does not roll off the cliff even though this would release potential energy, because in order to do so it would first have to roll uphill over the log, and this would mean an increase of energy.

Most of life's energy is drawn from reactions essentially similar to the reaction of methane with oxygen. However, in living processes the energy is released gently, more like a gurgling brook than a roaring waterfall. Let us consider how the electrons in the hydrogen atoms of food flow downhill to the "sea" of atmospheric oxygen. In living cells, the process takes place in microscopic bodies known as mitochondria (singular, mitochondrion). The structure of these is only beginning to be understood. They are like tiny organic transistor radios, through which electrons flow. The chemistry of the body is built around the flow of electrons, which after all is only an electric current.

These mitochondria are the original automation machines. They contain compounds known as enzymes, organic catalysts which lower the energy humps so that chemical reactions vital to life can proceed more rapidly. It is interesting that three of the substances used to fortify bread, namely niacin, riboflavin, and iron, are necessary in the diet because they are part of the huge enzyme molecules which carry hydrogen atoms from our food to the oxygen we breathe to form water and release energy. First, two hydrogen atoms are taken from the food molecule and passed to the niacin. They are then passed to the riboflavin. Then they pass on hand-over-hand to a series of iron compounds known as cytochromes, which finally transfer them to oxygen from the air to make water. In essence the reaction ends where the methane burning reaction did, with formation of water and carbon dioxide, and the release of energy. Some of this energy is released as heat which keeps us warm, and some is stored as chemical energy to do chemical work in our body processes and to provide our muscles with energy of motion.

It is calculated that the average man makes about one pint of water a day this way. This is called water of metabolism, and is not to be confused with water which one drinks or eats in foods. If this water produced by humans alone (not counting the many other forms of life) were placed in a river, it would flow at the rate of 400 million gallons a day. Many small desert animals never drink any liquid water in their lives; they meet their needs by water synthesis. Camels store fat in their humps and use it to produce water this way. Of course early man did not know that he was deriving energy from his food by these chemical reactions. It was not until the eighteenth century that man was confronted directly with a need for a scientific understanding of energy.

Before the eighteenth century, the people of the world had few labor-saving machines. They did their work much as it had been done since the time of the Pharaohs, tilling their fields with crude implements, cutting grain with sickles, and threshing it with flails. Clothing was woven on hand looms, and boards were cut from logs with hand saws and smoothed with block planes. Right up to the time of Isaac Newton (1642-1727 A. D.) most of the manufacturing was done by muscle power. The word "manufacture" means "made by hand."

About 1760, something began to happen which changed this situation. In a single generation there occurred changes more far-reaching than any which had been known in all the previous history of mankind. People worked with machines instead of with their muscles. The first to grasp the significance of this change and write about it was Arnold Toynbee (1852-1883). He was the first to use the term "The Industrial Revolution."

To understand how this Industrial Revolution came about we have to look into certain scientific discoveries which preceded it and made it possible. Robert Boyle (1627-1691) made discoveries concerning the behavior of gases, and invented a vacuum pump; and one of his assistants invented a steam engine. Isaac Newton introduced a new mathematical technique called the integral calculus. Without this scientific background the Industrial Revolution could not have happened.

Prior to this time, man had used an occasional windmill, waterwheel, or treadmill, but most work had been done by arduous human toil. So long as man could do work only with his muscles, his productive capacity was severely limited. It was not until a workable steam engine appeared that men had a significant replacement for human muscles. With the invention of the steam engine, and its application, productive capacity suddenly expanded.

The first industrial machines were steam pumps, used to pump water out of the coal mines of England. Disregarding Hero's toy precursor of jet propulsion, the steam engine appears to have been invented near the end of the seventeenth century by Denys Papin, a Frenchman in the employ of Robert Boyle, and independently by Thomas Savery, an Englishman. In 1707 Papin built a steamboat, which was destroyed by an angry mob of sailors. Papin himself narrowly missed death at their hands. Most of the early attempts to use steam power were foiled by attacks of the workers whose muscle power was displaced.

As time went on, and the British mine shafts were sunk deeper, there finally came a time when pumping the water out of the pits was beyond the capacity of muscle-power. It was also beyond the capacity of the primitive steam pumps. The first water pumps used successfully in the mines were made by a blacksmith, Thomas Newcomen (1663-1729), who designed a piston steam engine. Mr. Watt (1736-1819) came into the picture much later, and only then by making improvements on the Newcomen design. This made possible the removal of water from the mines, and the hoisting out of coal in greater quantities; it also increased the demand for coal, not only to run the engines but to smelt the iron with which to make the engines and the machines for the engines to run. Thus began a cycle of industrial expansion which has not yet ceased. This development meant that matter, in the form of coal, now had acquired the possibility of doing work, hitherto limited to muscle power. Out of this change arose technological problems of designing engines to be as efficient as possible.

It was Robert Boyle who discovered that there is "a spring in the air" and it is this elasticity of the gaseous state which made possible those early steam engines, as well as the modern automobile. Boyle's Law is back of the "kinetic molecular theory," and out of it has arisen fundamental concepts concerning the nature of matter, heat and energy.

The old physics of forces was unable to cope with this new situation, which involved evolution of heat as well as performance of mechanical work. Not all of the energy went into useful work. Fortunately, the new methods of the integral calculus were at hand, and they served to make possible the calculations without which an understanding of the heat engine would have been very difficult.

Kinetic molecular theory states that gases are made up of tiny, perfectly elastic particles (molecules), which are in ceaseless rapid motion, colliding with each other and with the walls of the container. "Perfectly elastic" means that when colliding with the walls of the container they bounce back without slowing down, something which a bouncing ball does not do. Their total impact upon the walls of a vessel is known as pressure, and their rate of motion is the basis of temperature. Thus, if gas molecules are in more rapid motion, this is expressed by saying that the gas is hotter. The same principle applies to liquids and solids, although liquids are more restricted in their movements and solids still more restricted.

From this theory one might consider an electric hot plate, for example, to be a kind of shaking machine. When electrons flow through the heating coils, the resistance to electron flow causes the metal atoms to shake more and more rapidly. If a tea kettle is placed on the hot plate, this shaking motion is translated to the water in the kettle, so that it begins to shake also. Soon the molecules of water are shaking so violently that some of them begin flying off into the air, and we say that the water is boiling. Thus heat energy, at the molecular level, is really an aspect of mechanical energy, the energy of motion.

This can be demonstrated by filling a vacuum bottle half full of water, and allowing it to stand uncapped until everything is at room temperature. A thermometer must be obtained which reads in tenths of a degree. The thermometer is inserted in the water, and carefully stirred around in the water until the temperature reading does not change. The temperature is recorded. The thermometer is removed, the vacuum bottle is stoppered, and it is shaken vigorously for at least five minutes. Then the stopper is removed, the thermometer is inserted, and the temperature recorded again. It is possible by this means to obtain a water temperature several tenths of a degree higher than before, demonstrating an actual conversion of mechanical energy into heat energy.

It finally became clear to scientists of the eighteenth century that a certain amount of coal was equivalent to a certain amount of work. This was because the heat it produced could do a certain amount of work. Therefore, a certain amount of matter, because of the energy which could be derived from it, represented a certain capacity to do work. Thus energy was defined as the capacity to do work.

Energy as a scientific concept suddenly became much more important. This chain reaction, the burning of coal in steam engines, meant a whole new world had opened to man, a world of abundant power and abundant goods. The excitement in those days about steam power was akin to the excitement in the present about nuclear power. A new science was created to deal with the transformations of energy. And because its first big application was to the steam engine, using <u>thermal</u> energy to produce <u>dynamic</u> energy, the science was named thermodynamics.

As the Industrial Revolution slowly swept over England, Europe, and the United States, and knowledge of the thermodynamics of mechanical engines developed, some scientists began to be curious about the thermodynamics of human engines. They worked first with farm animals, and found the same relations to hold which applied to steam engines. That is, from a given amount of feed, according to the heat it could produce when burned in a calorimeter, the animal could by its processes of digestion and metabolism derive a certain amount of heat plus work. The same results were obtained with humans.

In animals this process of respiration is accomplished without either an explosion or a flame. It occurs very gently and efficiently at body temperature. As a source of energy to provide heat and to do work in the human, it had already antedated the steam engine and coal stoves by perhaps two million years. Lavoisier (1734-1794), a French chemist who taught Mr. DuPont how to make gunpowder, announced in 1780 that "respiration is combustion, just as truly as if it were charcoal burning in the air." This was at that time a bold statement, and it might conceivably have resulted in his burning at the stake for heresy. As it turned out, however, times had changed, and he ended up being beheaded on the guillotine with the explanation that France had no need for scientists.

Benjamin Thompson was born in Massachusetts in 1753. He was a most versatile scientist and inventor. He became Count Rumford. He invented many wonderful things still in use today, including baking powder, a fireplace that did not "smoke," and the drip coffee pot. While supervising the boring of cannon, it happened one day that the drill became dull, and as a consequence the cannon barrel became quite hot. Count Rumford had the capacity of recognizing the significance of an observation not sought after, known as serendipity. He saw clearly an important new discovery, now known as "the mechanical equivalent of heat." It was already known from steam engine experiments that a certain amount of heat, obtained from a certain amount of coal burned to produce steam, could do a certain amount of work. Now he proved that this is true in the opposite direction as well: a certain amount of work can be converted into a certain, definite, equivalent amount of heat.

In order to measure amounts of heat, a unit of heat was devised. It is the amount of heat required to raise the temperature of one pound of water one degree Fahrenheit, and it is called the British thermal unit (B. t. u.). A laboratory unit in the metric system, the calorie, is smaller. One B. t. u. equals 252 calories.

It soon became apparent that the quantity of energy in any form, whether thermal energy (heat), mechanical energy (work), electrical energy, chemical energy, etc., is always the product of two factors. These factors are (1) A potential factor, which tells us how hard the force is applied; and (2) A capacity factor, which tells us how far through "distance" the force extends.

Perhaps our most familiar example is mechanical work, which is force times distance. In mechanical work, "force" is the potential factor, which tells how hard we push; and "distance" is the capacity factor, which tells how far we go. Once this idea becomes clear, it can be readily applied to thinking about other kinds of work. Every kind of potential factor is always a tendency for something to escape from a zone of greater density to a zone of lesser density. Thus volts, the potential factor for electrical work, is the tendency for electrons to escape from a region of greater electron density (concentration) to a region where there are fewer electrons. Temperature is the tendency for heat to escape from a hotter place toward a colder place, and temperature is the potential factor for thermal energy or heat quantity.

If a large bowl containing a mixture of ice and water is allowed to stand, it will reach equilibrium at a temperature of 32°F. Let us perform an experiment by heating a soldering iron to redness in a gas flame, and plunging it quickly into the ice water. If this is done rapidly, no steam escapes. The soldering iron cools down, but the ice water mixture does not heat up. After stirring the temperature is found by means of a thermometer to be at 32°F. We know that the iron contained heat. The heat escaped. The heat was not used to raise the temperature of the water. Where did the heat go? The answer is that the heat was turned into another channel: it increased the capacity factor.

Heat quantity is expressed in calories, Q; and the potential factor for heat quantity is temperature, T. Potential factor times capacity factor must equal Q. What can be multiplied by T to give Q? The answer is Q/T. The German physicist, Clausius, named this capacity factor "entropy", from the Greek word "trope" meaning to turn. The symbol for entropy is S. The increase in entropy, that is, the change in entropy, is indicated by use of the Greek letter delta: Δ, thus $\Delta S = \frac{Q}{T}$. Multiplying both sides of the equation by T, we have $Q = T \Delta S$. In words, this means, the calories of energy unavailable to do useful work, equals the (absolute) temperature times the change in entropy.

Probably the reason entropy seems difficult to comprehend is the fact that there is no sense perception for entropy. We can perceive temperature, pressure, etc. directly, but not entropy. Nevertheless it is just as real as any other factor in thermodynamics. There is no need to think about ideas of randomness, mixed-up-ness, disorder, etc., in order to think of entropy. It was a perfectly good thermodynamic function before there were any such notions, and it is not dependent upon any theory of the structure of matter. It is the place where the heat goes when ice melts to form water at the same temperature, and it is the place where the heat goes when water at the boiling temperature forms vapor at the same temperature. There is nothing the least bit mysterious about it.

A law of science is an experience summary, and nothing more. The laws of thermodynamics are good examples. They cannot be proved, and yet all scientists have absolute faith in them. The first law of thermodynamics, when it was first proposed, seemed intuitive and even in accord with religious belief, and consequently it was accepted without dissent. It is the law of conservation of matter and energy. One way to say it is: Matter (and energy) can neither be created nor destroyed. Since matter is only a form of energy, one can simply state: The total energy content of the Universe remains constant. Philosophically, it is inconceivable that this is so, and equally inconceivable that it is not so.

Every system (the part of the Universe chosen for consideration) contains within itself an internal energy content. One does not know the absolute quantity of this internal energy; but it may be possible to measure how much it changes as the system changes from an initial state to a final state. It is human experience that this change in internal energy is independent of the pathway taken. Let us consider as an illustration, a small weight and a heavier weight, hung on a rope over a pulley (Fig. 10).

The larger weight will descend, and in so doing it will do an amount of work W by moving the smaller weight up a distance D times a force F. If a brake is applied, this will decrease the force F and hence less work will be done in moving the weight distance D. But the change in internal energy will remain constant. What became of the extra energy? The answer is that it was converted into heat Q, which was absorbed by the brake drum in the system. Summarizing this experience, the first law of thermodynamics states that the change in internal energy, $\Delta E = Q - W$.

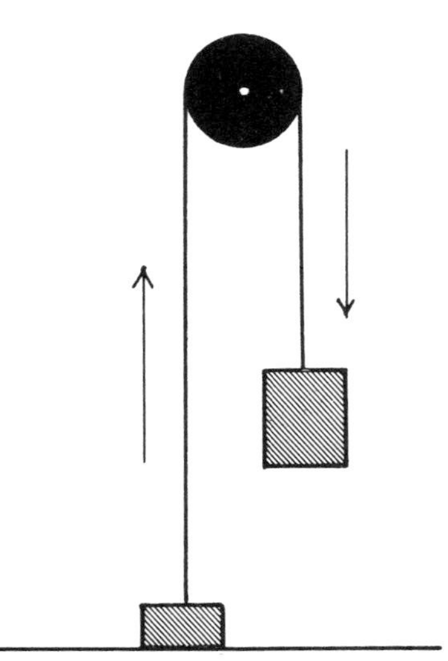

FIG. 10. DIAGRAM ILLUSTRATING CHANGE IN INTERNAL ENERGY.

Unlike the first law, the second law of thermodynamics is not intuitive, and it was resisted from the beginning. It was needed because thermodynamics has a direction, the direction of increasing entropy, and the first law fails to indicate a direction. Something was needed to show that we could not have $-\Delta E = W - Q$. The second law states that the entropy of a system never decreases by itself. Another way to say it is, that heat will never pass spontaneously from a colder body to a hotter body. If we heat one end of an iron rod and cool the other end, then heat will flow from the hot end toward the cold end and not the other way around. Ice will melt and water will evaporate spontaneously, because this is in the direction of increasing entropy, but water vapor will not condense and freeze to ice unless heat is removed from it by some outside force, such as a mechanical refrigerator.

We have previously discussed the three phases of water in terms of relative degree of hydrogen bonding. The three phases also represent three different entropy contents. Entropy is the invisible reservoir of heat which keeps climates equable and makes life tolerable on earth. It is entropy which absorbs the heat when a heat wave comes, so that we do not die of high temperature. It is also entropy which releases heat in an emergency when a cold wave comes, so that we do not freeze to death. Most of the stability of climate is maintained by this bank account of entropy in the water on the earth and in its atmosphere.

Since entropy tends always to increase, it has been called "time's arrow." That is, one might say that time is that which passes as entropy increases, and also that the forward direction of time is that direction which leads to entropy increase. The driving force in any system is to reach minimum free energy, and maximum entropy. Clausius stated that the energy of the world is constant, but that the entropy of the world strives to reach a maximum. If this is so, obviously the world is running down.

Living organisms, and human beings, behave contrary to the general tendency, because they represent highly organized structures, in which entropy actually decreases. Some have speculated that living things violate the second law of thermodynamics, but this is not so. The second law refers only to systems which do not get outside help, and living things are able to lower their entropy only at the expense of a greater increase in entropy in their environment. It has been said that they feed on "negative entropy." The second law still holds.

The second law says in effect that it is impossible to make a perpetual motion machine. Yet people never give up trying. The U. S. Patent Office refuses to examine models of alleged perpetual motion machines. The second law of thermodynamics has never been proved, and there is not the slightest likelihood that it will be proved. But all attempts to disprove it, and there have been many, have failed. That is why scientists believe it is true.

We have believed so long that matter can be neither created nor destroyed, that it is difficult to comprehend that matter actually can be annihilated and energy take its place. Nevertheless, it is true that energy can be converted into matter, and matter can be converted into energy. This sounded like fiction back in 1905 when Einstein stated that mass and energy were equivalent, and no one paid much attention to his equation $E = mc^2$, in which E is energy in ergs, m is mass in grams, and c is the speed of light in centimeters per second, a very large number (3×10^{10} or thirty billion). But it is not fiction. If we were to burn a kilogram (2. 2 pounds) of coal and get all of the heat energy out of this chemical reaction, such as we did in the steam engines previously discussed, this would yield about 8. 5 kilowatt hours of electricity. But if we took this same small chunk of coal, and converted its matter entirely into energy, calculating from Einstein's equation, the yield would be twenty-five billion kilowatt hours. Here we have used certain terms, such as erg, gram, second, etc., without definition. To go into this further would carry us too far for the present purposes.

The concept of energy took on new meaning at 5:30 a. m. 16 July, 1945 in a remote section of the Alamogordo Air Base 120 miles southeast of Albuquerque, New Mexico, when "a small amount of matter was made to release the energy of the universe locked up within the atom from the beginning of time."

Here is how this momentous occasion was described by a War Department release:

"Tension reached a tremendous pitch in the control room as the deadline approached. The several observation points in the area were tied in to the control room by radio ...The time signals, 'minus 20 minutes, minus 15 minutes,' and on and on increased the tension to the breaking point as the group in the control room ... held their breaths, all praying with the intensity of the moment which will live forever with each man who was there. At 'minus 45 seconds,' robot mechanism took over and from that point on the whole great complicated mass of intricate mechanism was in operation without human control.

"At the appointed time there was a blinding flash lighting up the whole area brighter than the brightest daylight. A mountain range three miles from the observation point stood out in bold relief. Then came a tremendous sustained roar and a heavy pressure wave which knocked down two men outside the control center. Immediately thereafter, a huge multi-colored surging cloud boiled to an altitude of over 40,000 feet. Clouds in its path disappeared. Soon the shifting substratosphere winds dispersed the now grey mass.

"The steel tower had been entirely vaporized. Where the tower had stood, there was a huge sloping crater. Dazed but relieved at the success of their tests, the scientists promptly marshalled their forces to estimate the strength of America's new weapon ... A significant aspect, recorded by the press, was the experience of a blind girl near Albuquerque many miles from the scene, who, when the flash of the test lighted the sky before the explosion could be heard, exclaimed, What was that? ... The feeling of the entire assembly, even the uninitiated, was of profound awe ... We were reaching into the unknown and we did not know what might come of it. It can safely be said that most of those present were praying--and praying harder than they had ever prayed before ... All seemed to feel that they had been present at the birth of a new age --The Age of Atomic Energy--and felt their profound responsibility to help in guiding into right channels the tremendous forces which had been unlocked for the first time in history ...

"The effects could well be called unprecedented, magnificent, beautiful, stupendous and terrifying. No man-made phenomenon of such tremendous power had ever occurred before. The lighting effects beggared description. The whole country was lighted by a searing light with the intensity many times that of the midday sun. It was golden, purple, violet, gray, and blue. It lighted every peak, crevasse and ridge of the nearby mountain range with a clarity and beauty the great poets dream about but describe most poorly and inadequately. Thirty seconds after, the explosion came first, the air blast pressing hard against the people and things, to be followed almost immediately by the strong, sustained, awesome roar which warned of doomsday and made us feel that we puny things were blasphemous to dare tamper with the forces heretofore reserved to the Almighty. . ."

From Appendix 6, Atomic Energy for Military Purposes, H. D. Smyth, Princeton University Press, 1945.

Energy is released from the nucleus of an atom by "fission" or by "fusion." Thus energy is released from heavy atoms, such as uranium, by splitting the nucleus into smaller parts. Energy is obtained from a light atom, such as the isotopes of hydrogen, by "fusing" two or more nuclei together to create a new element with a heavier nucleus.

Although nuclear energy is usually thought of as something new, it is actually the source of the energy we derive from the sun. The amount of sun energy which reaches one square mile of the earth every day is equal to that which would be obtained by burning 3,600 tons of coal. The sun derives this energy from nuclear fusion. At tremendous temperature and pressure, four hydrogen atoms fuse to make one helium atom, and the mass which is left over because the atomic weight of helium is less than 4X the atomic weight of hydrogen, disappears in the form of energy. It is this energy which makes life possible.

Uncontrolled release of nuclear energy produces the violent results which made the mushroom clouds which have become a symbol of the Atomic Age. But much more important in the long run, it is to be hoped, are the peacetime uses of atomic energy. It is possible to build power plants which use nuclear energy to provide electric power for whole cities;

in fact such power plants already are in operation. A small amount of nuclear fuel can power a submarine or ship at sea for years without refueling. It is impossible to overestimate the importance to mankind of the radioactive "tracer" elements which have revolutionized knowledge of medicine, biochemistry, and biological sciences in general. In any country, the standard of living bears a close correlation to the available power consumption per capita. Nations which do not have water power, coal, oil, or other resources have not been able to industrialize. Atomic power plants will make this possible. It is estimated they can produce power as cheaply as the conventional power plants. It is predicted that we are entering upon a new era in civilization based upon atomic power, supplanting power from falling water and the fossil fuels such as coal, petroleum, and natural gas. This will rearrange the balance of nations because atomic power plants enable a nation without natural power resources to produce the power needed to industrialize. Atomic power release has placed within the hands of mankind power of a magnitude far beyond anything ever dreamed of, and not matched by commensurate spiritual power needed to keep from using this power to wipe out the human race. It is something like giving a box of dynamite and a box of matches to a group of two-year-old children. If humanity survives, it is also predicted that use of atomic power will be only an interim before it in turn is supplanted by power obtained directly from the Sun. Technology in this area is making rapid advances.

Energy is released from an atom by giving off particles from its nucleus. Atoms to which this happens end up with different atomic numbers, and hence actually become different elements. The old goal of the early alchemists, to convert one element into another, is now commonplace.

Some elements present in the rocks of our Earth are disintegrating spontaneously in this manner. They are said to be radioactive. The principal elements doing this are uranium, thorium, radium, and actinium. Each has a heavy nucleus, with a complicated structure, too complicated for detailed consideration in this book. It is common for a "parent" nucleus such as one of these to decompose, yielding a "daughter" nucleus, which in turn decomposes, and so on and so on. This sets up a shower or cascade of radioactive intermediate elements, and the disintegration continues until finally elements with stable nuclei are obtained. In this manner, radium, actinium, and thorium all start from isotopes of uranium, and each produces a radioactive series which ends up with a stable isotope of lead. From the proportions of uranium and lead present, geologists are able to compute the age of the various rock formations.

The above paragraph refers to natural radioactivity, something we have always had with us. However, there is now a great deal of artificial radioactivity, a consequence of the release of nuclear energy on a large scale, and this radioactive "waste" has become a matter of world-wide concern. Radioactive isotopes of nearly any element can now be produced where there are nuclear reactors. Remember that an isotope is an element which has the usual number of protons (the atomic number of that element), but has a different number of neutrons. Some of these isotopes are stable, but the ones to which we refer happen to be unstable and hence radioactive.

The rate of "decay" of a radioactive element is measured by means of its "half-life." This is the time required for one-half of the atoms among a given large number of these atoms to disintegrate. We do not use "whole-life" because the whole-life of a radioactive element would be infinity, which is rather meaningless in this case. It would be like the theoretical time at which a ball would stop bouncing. Suppose we find that when we drop a golf ball on a concrete walk, each time it bounces to one-half its previous height. Theoretically, it would never stop bouncing, because one-half of something never equals zero.

We learned previously that the half-life of free neutrons is only thirteen minutes. This is an extremely unstable particle. At the opposite extreme is ordinary uranium, with a half-life of 4,670,000,000 years! Carbon-14 has a half-life of 5600 years. It occurs in nature, and the measurement of its radioactivity in archeological materials, etc., containing carbon is the basis of the carbon dating method. Cobalt-60 has a half-life of 5.3 years, which puts it in the dangerous class insofar as fallout is concerned, because it is not short enough to disappear rapidly, and not long enough to be unlikely to disintegrate within a human body during a lifetime. Iodine-131 has a half-life of eight days; it is used in medical treatment and research, as is phosphorus-32, with a half-life of 14.3 days.

Radioactivity has been present throughout the existence of life, and is not something entirely new because of nuclear explosions. Many drinking water sources which have been in use for years contain radioactive elements. Bricks are slightly radioactive, and persons who live in brick houses or work in brick buildings are thus exposed to more radiation than in wooden structures, but this is not something to start worrying about. Many areas have natural radioactivity in their rock formations. Everybody receives radiation from cosmic rays. Those who live at high altitudes receive much more than those who live at sea level. Some authorities state that nobody anywhere in the world would probably receive as much radiation from test fallout during an entire lifetime as they receive from cosmic rays. If there is any immediate danger of injury from fallout from nuclear explosions in the atmosphere, it seems to center about one radioactive product, which is strontium-90. The number 90, as is the case with each of these numbers as used above, refers to the atomic mass, in other words, the sum of the number of protons plus neutrons in that particular isotope of the element. Strontium-90 has a half-life in the dangerous region of about thirty years, but even more significant is the fact that it settles in the bones, where it can cause bone cancer and leukemia. If the need should ever arise, effective methods of removing it from milk or other contaminated sources have been developed.

This chapter ends our discussion. Let us briefly review what has been said. We have discussed one's image of himself and the world around him, and his image of science and the scientist. We have tried to improve the image of science. We have seen that science describes the behavior of the physical world in terms of four mental concepts, without confusing the concepts with reality or assuming that the physical world is the real world in its entirety. We have discussed the concepts of space and time and discovered that we live in a very strange world. We have discussed the concepts of matter and discovered that the solidness of matter is an illusion, and that matter is actually only a manifestation of space-time localized energy. In short, we have discovered that things are not what they seem.

We are living in a world in which Materialism is rapidly enthralling the human race. This belief in Materialism is founded on the science of the nineteenth century. Meanwhile, contemporary science has left such a concept far behind. In the present century, space, time, and matter have largely lost their reality. They have become more like the television picture tube which merely scans reality. They are like the contrails left by the jet plane so high in the sky that it cannot be seen. We do not actually see the plane; all we see is where it has been.

Although we have such word labels as "atom bomb," and "Atomic Energy Commission," scientists know that the way in which we at present conceive of matter existing in the form of "atoms" is little more than a marvelous fiction of the human mind. One may see models, pictures, or diagrams of what purports to be an atom, knowing that each of these is incorrect. No matter who tries to picture an atom, contemporary science tells us, the result is as if it were conceived by an artist in a studio for making animated cartoon movies. Our concept of matter has reached a point at which it can be described only in terms of mathematical equations which most persons cannot understand. Quite literally, it has become impossible for anybody to think correctly about the structure of matter.

Matter, the scientists tell us, is some sort of waves or vibrations of energy. Not <u>something</u> waving, just the waves themselves. Like the grin left behind by the Cheshire-Cat, in <u>Alice's Adventures in Wonderland</u>:

"Did you say 'pig', or 'fig'?" said the Cat.

"I said 'pig'," replied Alice; "and I wish you wouldn't keep appearing and vanishing so suddenly: you make one quite giddy!"

"All right," said the Cat; and this time it vanished quite slowly, beginning with the end of the tail, and ending with the grin, which remained some time after the rest of it had gone.

"Well! I've often seen a cat without a grin," thought Alice; "but a grin without a cat. It's the most curious thing I ever saw in all my life!"

When we perceive matter with our senses, all we really know is that there is <u>something</u> out there. Its true nature eludes us. We weave our own image of physical reality, using only electron waves as the shuttles of our mental looms. And so the reality of matter, like the reality of space and time, has slipped through our fingers. Matter and energy are the same thing. We do not know what energy is. All we know is what it can do. If we may paraphrase Shakespeare:

These our atoms, were all wave functions and
  Are melted into air, into thin air:
And, like the baseless fabric of our concepts,
  The cloud-capp'd towers, the gorgeous palaces,
The solemn temples, the great globe itself,
  Yea, all which it inherit, shall dissolve
And, like this insubstantial pageant faded,
  Leave not a rack behind. We are such stuff
As dreams are made on, and our little life
  Is rounded with a sleep.

George Berkeley was an Anglican bishop who lived from 1685 to 1753. The element Berkelium, atomic number 97, discovered in 1950, was named after him. Inadvertently, of course, since it was named after Berkeley, California which in turn was named for the bishop. Something of the present dilemma of scientists in trying to communicate what they have discovered about matter reminds one of a passage in Berkeley's <u>Dialogues</u> (1711):

EUPHRANOR: Tell me, Alciphron, can you discern the doors, windows and battlements of that same castle?

ALCIPHRON: I cannot. At this distance it seems only a small round tower.

EUPHRANOR: But I, who have been at it, know that it is no small round tower, but a large square building with battlements and turrets, which it seems you do not see.

ALCIPHRON: What will you infer from thence?

EUPHRANOR: I would infer that the very object which you strictly and properly perceive by sight is not that thing which is several miles distant. Is it not plain, therefore, that neither the castle, the planet nor the cloud, which you see here, are those real ones which you suppose to exist at a distance?

Questions

1. What was man's first source of energy to keep warm and to do work?
2. Explain how the energy cycle of life involves the shuttling back and forth of electrons between carbon orbitals and oxygen orbitals.
3. What is meant by an "energy hump" and why is it important to life?
4. What is meant by water of metabolism?
5. Name two scientific discoveries which led to the steam engine?
6. What new science was developed to deal with work produced from heat?
7. Define temperature and pressure in terms of kinetic molecular theory.
8. How can conversion of mechanical energy into heat be demonstrated?
9. What was the Industrial Revolution?

10. Explain Lavoisier's statement that respiration is combustion.
11. What is meant by the mechanical equivalent of heat?
12. What is a potential factor? A capacity factor? Give examples of each.
13. Where does the heat "go" when ice melts to form water at the same temperature?
14. What are the first and second laws of thermodynamics?
15. What proof is there that matter can be converted into energy?
16. How long has mankind been getting energy from nuclear energy sources?
17. What is meant by radioactivity, unstable isotope, and half-life?
18. Why is strontium-90 considered dangerous in fallout from explosions?
19. Has this book changed your thinking concerning the realness of material things? If so, has this new understanding of the nature of matter made you feel uneasy?

Suggested Reading

Abbott, E. A. Flatland. Blackwell, Oxford, 1944.

Allen, D. S., and Ordway, R. J. Physical Science. D. Van Nostrand Co., Princeton, N. J. 1960.

Boulding, K. E. The Image. University of Michigan Press. 1956.

Clareson, T. D. Science and Society. Harper & Brothers, New York, 1961.

Christiansen, G. S. and Garrett, P. H. Structure and Change. W. H. Freeman & Co., San Francisco. 1960.

Coulson, C. A. Science and the Idea of God. Cambridge University Press, New York. 1958.

Eddington, A. S. The Nature of the Physical World. The Macmillan Co., New York, 1929.

Gray, D. E., and Coutts, J. W. Man and His Physical World. D. Van Nostrand Co., Princeton, N. J. 1958.

Hoffman, B. The Strange Story of the Quantum. Dover Publications, New York. 1959.

Krauskopf, K., and Beiser, A. The Physical Universe. McGraw-Hill Book Co., New York. 1960.

Schneer, C. J. The Search for Order. Harper & Brothers, New York. 1960.

Schroedinger, E. What Is Life? & Other Scientific Essays. Doubleday & Co., Garden City, New York, 1956.

Slabaugh, W. H., and Butler, A. B. College Physical Science. Prentice-Hall, Englewood Cliffs, N. J. 1958.

Standen, A. Science Is a Sacred Cow. E. P. Dutton & Co., New York, 1950.

Swenson, H. N. and Woods, J. E. Physical Science for Liberal Arts Students. John Wiley & Sons, New York. 1957.

Winslow, E. C. Basic Principles of Chemistry. D. Van Nostrand Co., New York. 1958.

Wistar, R. Man and His Physical Universe. John Wiley & Sons, New York. 1960.

Motion Pictures: 16 mm. color sound films, Bell Science Series:
(a) About Time. (b) Gateways to the Mind. (c) Our Mr. Sun. These may be obtained for free showing to groups through any Bell Telephone office. They illustrate many of the concepts and principles described in this book.

Index